BINOCULARS
and people

Brin Best

Published by Biosphere Publications
An imprint of Innovation for Education Ltd
9 Throstle Nest Close
Otley
LS21 2RR
West Yorkshire
UK

Design by Character Design, Hereford

Printed and bound in the UK by Amadeus Press

ISBN 978-1-904841-03-6

Cover image: Kerry Low

DEDICATION

This book is dedicated to those brave men and women who lost their lives during the terrible military conflicts described in this book. Many of these people would have used binoculars as part of their standard equipment during their time serving their countries. Although tens of thousands of these instruments returned home, following military service, this was a luxury denied to the millions of people who fell in action.

'The binocular cannot only become part of the eyes, it can become part of the heart too'
                                                                    ANONYMOUS

CONTENTS

ACKNOWLEDGEMENTS

I WANT TO thank all those people who have made this book possible. The scarcity of books on binoculars has meant that I have been especially reliant on the wisdom of binocular collectors, scientific historians and a host of other people in putting this publication together.

Chris Clarke deserves a special mention because he was the person who first introduced me to eBay. The book project only gathered pace once I had realised that this auction site would allow me to sample myriad binoculars from around the world.

Peter Abrahams kindly allowed me to join his invaluable email list on the history of binoculars, helping me to get in touch with a range of experts and enthusiasts. His venture has produced a most impressive compendium of information on binoculars, put together by many of the world's leading collectors.

Steve Harris, formerly a director at CleySpy, has been a major source of support and encouragement since the project began. He has generously shared his enormous knowledge of optics, and has indulged my passion for binoculars in extended viewing sessions and lively conversations at his home overlooking the North Norfolk saltmarshes.

Paul Marriot and the rest of the CleySpy staff welcomed me into their cavernous shop and allowed me to test hundreds of different models without a hint of irritation. They also provided much additional information on modern binoculars and the behaviour of people who are choosing and buying new optics.

I have also benefited from discussions with Bernie Starky and John McLoughlin at the In Focus shop in Denby Dale, as well as being able to test some interesting optics which they have recommended. David Uwins of Ace Optics and the staff at Bass and Bligh, Harrogate and Rother Valley Optics provided valuable additional information and allowed me to test a further range of binoculars.

Renze de Vries has helped me to shape many of my ideas around the use of binoculars and has also swapped or loaned numerous optics, allowing me to discover special models that I would not otherwise have encountered. His regular lively emails have been a constant source of interest.

Eric Wood sold me my first eBay binocular and has provided some wonderful models in the intervening years. His knowledge of Zeiss and Leica/Leitz binoculars in particular has proved invaluable.

Robert Gregory's support for the project has been very welcome. As well being the UK's most published binocular author, with five books to his name, Robert has been extremely generous in sharing his knowledge and enthusiasm for binoculars. I have greatly enjoyed our conversations and testing sessions, and would also like to express my gratitude for the many binoculars that Robert has passed on to me.

Niall McLaren has also been very generous in sharing his wide knowledge of binoculars with me, especially those with military backgrounds. He also provided wonderful examples of various binoculars with a history. His contribution to the book has been significant.

I thank Jeremy Holland, Maurice Marchant of CleySpy and Tony Kay of Optrep for repairing and cleaning numerous binoculars, allowing me to enjoy them in original optical condition as I researched the book.

I want to thank all those people who sold or gave me binoculars for my ever-changing reference collection, which at times approached 500 examples. Although too numerous to mention here, the previous owners of all these binoculars have helped to educate me on the pros and cons of the multitude of makes and models that have been produced. In some cases they have also provided invaluable advice on the performance of different models. I also thank the following who made specific suggestions for what might be included in the 'Landmark binocular' panels and other helpful remarks: Peter Abrahams, Fred Matthies, Geoffrey Samuel and Tilman Taube.

The book benefited immeasurably from the contributions of the people who allowed their own special stories of binoculars to be told. All are named in the text in the appropriate places. I also thank various members of my family and extended family for discussions on binoculars, which helped to clarify their use on both sides of the Atlantic.

I am pleased to be able to thank a range of people who provided perspectives on binoculars from their particular part of the world. They are Jem Coady (UK), Tom Fowler (UK), Paul Gumm (UK), Ed Huff (USA), Michael Kaczor (Australia), Stephen Ingraham (USA), Christopher Lowe (UK), Ian Malcom (Canada), Rod Pendry (UK), Vin Robinson (UK), Debbie Stevens (USA), Angelo Tordaro (USA) and Ian Whitlock (UK),

The following generously allowed their photographs to appear in the book: Amanda Best, Crown Products Limited, Alex Gilbert, Groovy Norfolk, Andy Hay (RSPB Images), Marcella Hume, Rob Hume, Steve Kaluza, Pete Kinsella, Marit Bøe Larsen, Leica Camera AG, Kerry Low, Pamela McBirnie, Niall McLaren, Martin Mears, Derek Niemann, Jan Staller, Trinity Marine, Barbara Wood and Renze de Vries. Scott T. Price from the US Coast Guard headquarters in Washington provided helpful additional assistance sourcing binocular images.

Various people kindly agreed to look over parts of the manuscript in draft form, providing invaluable expertise to help me improve the accuracy and scope of the book. They are Peter Abrahams, Robert Gregory, Dr Jon Maxwell, Dr Holger Merlitz, Niall Maclaren, Dr Steven Sambrook, Renze de Vries, Tilman Taube and Steve Harris. Gill O'Donnell and Chris Robinson proof-read the entire manuscript, providing numerous corrections and additions that improved the book.

Ian Ashton was particularly helpful in searching out binocular advertisements, many of which appear in the book, and Sayaka Salembier helped to provide translations from Japanese into English.

I thank the following who provided valuable additional information for the book: Stella Rumbles (RSPB), Jörg Kaufmann (Leica Camera AG, Germany) and Tilman Taube (Leica Camera AG, Gemany).

I would like to thank the Royal Mail staff in Otley and the Parcelforce team in Leeds for safely delivering over 300 binoculars to me from all corners of the globe. It seems remarkable that not a single instrument was lost on its way to my house.

I am delighted that Kerry and Richard of Character Design were able to take on the design of the book. It would not be possible to find a more skilled, patient and efficient design team. The Amadeus Press printed the book with their customary efficiency.

I need to offer special thanks to my wife Amanda who has been unbelievable patient as I have worked on this project for the last four years. I knew things were getting out of hand when she started to dream about a secret society of binocular enthusiasts called 'the greens' of which I was apparently a founder member! At times it seemed like our house was literally overflowing with binoculars, and only a fool would need to add another example to his reference collection. That fool is lucky to have such a supportive wife, who has also been a faithful companion on so many trips to try out binoculars at nature reserves, sporting events and the theatre.

Finally I want to emphasise that I consider myself a writer with a passion for binoculars, rather than an authority in my own right. As such, while I have benefited greatly from the above-mentioned people I take full responsibility for any errors or omissions that remain. I would welcome correspondence and corrections and encourage you to get in touch if you have any information that will help to produce an even fuller account of the social history of binoculars at some point in the future. You can contact me by email at brinbest@hotmail.com, or by writing to me care of the publisher.

FOR THE COUNTLESS time Yuji Hyakutake gazes through his giant astronomical binoculars from the clear skies above Kagoshima Prefecture in southern Japan. Hyakutake, an amateur astronomer, has been searching for comets for months and has moved to this part of Japan partly because of its dark skies. He hopes that one day he will find a very special object – one that will bear his name forever. Hours pass by, some interesting celestial objects are spotted, but they turn out to be known heavenly bodies. Then a smudge comes into view that is not familiar to this veteran of the night sky. Close observation over a period of days eventually reveals this to be his holy grail – a comet! Hyakutake keeps observing the quadrant of the night sky over the coming weeks and is almost knocked over when he discovers another comet in almost exactly the same position as the first. His observation is confirmed by the National Astronomical Observatory of Japan the following day. While the first comet that Hyakutake found that year – now known idiosyncratically as C/1995 Y1 – never becomes visible to the naked eye, six weeks later the second produces one of the most stunning astronomical observations of a generation as Comet Hyakutake lights up the night sky over much of the northern hemisphere.

ON THE ICY peak of Cader Idris in Wales, National Park Warden David Williams scans the infamous Rattlers Gully, where a group of ice climbers are tackling a taxing ascent. He sees one of the team, Titch Kavanagh, who turns out to be a veteran of Alpine and Himalayan mountaineering, complete the climb. Then he looks away, sweeps back to the scene with his binocular and notices something falling through the air. 'Surely it's a bird,' he thinks? But the climber is not where he finished the climb and David has the terrible realisation that he must have fallen 140 feet to the bottom of the gully. An emergency call to the Royal Air Force sees a helicopter race to this dramatic part of Snowdonia and Titch airlifted to hospital in nearby Bangor. That observation and that call saves Titch's life. Though he spends a year in a coma and has to undergo multiple treatments for injuries to his head and hip, Titch eventually recovers from his terrible fall in Rattlers Gully. He is now back at work in Yorkshire – promoting men's health issues. It is three years since his accident and Titch is finally looking forward to telephoning David to thank him for that life-saving observation on the mountain.

SUN YONGLIAN LOOKS out across Yangshan Park from the rooftop of his home in a downtown district of Beijing. As he scans the scene with his binocular, Sun Yongolian fixes his eyes on countless bulldozed buildings. He is scared and lonely, for he has seen all of his neighbours evicted as the Chinese authorities clear the area ready for the forthcoming Olympics. Compensation has been provided, but many residents feel it is inadequate. Will he finally glimpse the ultimate eviction party arriving to clear this last dwelling? His home, which he shares with his wife Chen Zongxia and two members of her family, is located on the site of one of the last 'beautification projects' for the Olympic games. Three years ago this development site was a thriving traditional neighbourhood; now the only building not to be razed to the ground is Sun Yongolian's home. Although it has provided shelter for four generations of this proud Beijinger's family, the house is fragile in the face of the onslaught from the Chinese authorities. Sun Yongolian has built up crude defences to halt the approach of the bulldozers – but he cannot stop these mighty machines. As they scan the horizon, fearing that their world will soon literally fall apart, Sun Yongolian and his family are surer than ever that the Olympic dream has turned into a nightmare for those at the sharp end of the drive to modernise Beijing for the global spectacle to come.

Prologue

'Life moves pretty fast. If you don't stop and look around once in a while you could miss it.'

FERRIS BUELLER

IT IS IMPOSSIBLE to estimate the number of binoculars in use across the world today, but it must run into the tens of millions. They are now a ubiquitous consumer item and readily available at a price to suit almost everyone. Perhaps the reason why they have such an enduring appeal is the huge range of uses for binoculars. You can buy a binocular today and tomorrow begin a lifetime of birdwatching, start searching for the next undiscovered comet or study the facial expressions of the world's finest opera singers. And there are literally hundreds of other uses – only bounded by your imagination. Later in the book, however, we will see that the affordability of binoculars for the masses is very much a modern phenomenon. Indeed, this forms part of the fascinating history of binoculars and people's relationship with them.

Cultural significance

Binoculars have played a prominent role in both war and peace time, and their cultural significance has tended to be neglected in the past. Binoculars have provided people with some of the most exciting, moving or arresting experiences of their lives. Furthermore, the way in which people have benefited from, and interacted with, their binoculars over time tells its own special story, which also helps to cast light on our social history. Because binoculars tend to be kept in families and passed on to future generations, they often bring with them important family history and a link to the past. For some families, they are even treasured heirlooms which can conjure up memories which otherwise might be all too easily forgotten.

Of course binoculars are often beautiful objects in their own right. Some are even encrusted with diamonds or plated with gold to make them even more desirable. They are precision instruments, made to incredibly tight tolerances and designed to last for a lifetime. They often create a lasting impression and most people can remember the first time they looked through a really good binocular. All this adds to their allure and appreciation by a very wide range of people – and makes them worthy of a book of their own.

Binoculars are now firmly rooted in the public's imagination. They regularly appear in movies or help to add an extra dimension to novels. Visitors to the Lancashire coast are greeted by the celebrated statue of binocular-sporting comedian Eric Morecambe in the town from which he took his stage name;

another wonderfully-evocative statue of the nature conservation pioneer Sir Peter Scott stands within the boundary of the London Wetland Centre, his binoculars at the ready to get close up views of wildfowl. Anyone sat at a computer running one of the popular programs is only a few clicks away from the binocular icon that accompanies the 'find' function. Furthermore, users of the popular online payment facility Paypal are often greeted by silhouetted figures using binoculars as a metaphor for bargain searching. In these ways and many others, binoculars have found a place in our lives.

Introducing this book

There is a curious lack of literature on binoculars, especially in the English language. There is just one slim volume in English that deals with the history of these fascinating instruments (Watson 2004), and it scarcely mentions the social dimension of binoculars. Popular works on astronomy or natural history that might delve into some of the wonderful stories of people and their binoculars also tend to remain rather silent on this particular aspect of these optical aids. This book aims to fill that void.

Ever since I first looked through a binocular as a tiny child I have been captivated by how they can change your view of the world – how, as if by magic, they can make the invisible suddenly visible in three dimensions. As I grew older, I often found myself deep in conversation with binocular users from times of peace and war, fascinated to find out more. I also used binoculars increasingly myself for a wide range of hobbies and even in my career. During this time, I came to appreciate that there was a wonderful story behind binoculars and the way they have shaped people's lives and memories. The main aim of this book is to tell that story, set against the technological advances in binocular design across the centuries.

I have gone to considerable lengths to make the book user-friendly and to appeal to the general reader as well as the binocular connoisseur. I don't want what follows to appeal only to those technically-minded aficionados who understand what exit pupil diameters and eye relief measurements are about (there is a glossary at the back of the book dealing with these and other binocular terms). To achieve my aim I have illuminated the main text with a series of self-contained boxes and panels, some of which contain technical information which forms an important part of the story of binoculars. They include the following:

- **'Landmark binocular'** panels provide an opportunity to focus in detail on some of the more important models, or those with particularly enduring appeal to one or more user groups. Although I have canvassed opinion quite widely among binocular collectors over which models to include here, my final selection is clearly subjective and I make no excuses for including some of my own favourites.
- **'My binocular story'** entries allow individuals to place on record amusing, interesting, moving or quirky stories relating to their own experiences with binoculars.

- **'Binocular with a history'** features tell the stories of instruments that are reported to have an especially interesting past. Rather than question the historical accuracy of any information I was given by owners to create these, I prefer to offer them in their original form. Any inaccuracies that are subsequently uncovered form their own part of the social history of binoculars.

As this book has been written by an Englishman living in the UK, many of the stories relate to experiences in that country – though I have tried to include much information from outside my country too. North American readers may have to remind themselves of some of the key linguistic differences between the forms of English spoken on opposite sides of the Atlantic (for example, the type of sport played in England called football is known as 'soccer' in their continent). Unless otherwise mentioned all place names refer to locations in England.

Let us begin the book with an overview of the fascinating history of binoculars. This will help to provide the backdrop for the chapters that follow on more specific aspects of binoculars and their social history.

'If eyes are indeed the mirror of the soul, then binoculars can magnify our souls.'

JOHN BARSNESS

1 A short history of binoculars

The precise moment in time when a person first placed a binocular to their eyes is lost in history. Thanks to the work of early optical pioneers, the telescope had become a remarkable new tool for long range observation, bringing hitherto unseen objects and new worlds within the compass of the lucky few in the 16th century. It cannot be long after this that somebody – a scientist or somebody of considerable wealth or influence – hit upon the idea that more comfortable long range viewing would be possible when using two telescopes, one for each eye. That simple yet creative act of aligning two primitive telescopes side by side can be seen as the moment of birth of the binocular. And so began a fascinating four hundred year story of binocular viewing, that would see binoculars influence wars, change history, shape people's lives and allow humans to see the world as they have never seen it before. This chapter presents the major milestones in the history of binoculars, providing the landscape against which the story of binoculars and people can be set.

The launch of Zeiss prismatic binoculars in the 1890s represented the most important milestone since their invention almost three centuries earlier

THE EARLY RECORDED history of the binocular is closely linked to that of the telescope. Telescopes were reported in the years prior to 1600, but no documentary evidence for their existence exists until a Dutch patent application of October 1608. Hans Lippershey (1570-1619), a spectacle maker living in a part of the low countries that is now the Netherlands, applied for a patent application for a telescope that would grant him exclusive manufacturing rights for 30 years. Following testing by the patent authorities, Lippershey was asked to make a second type of instrument that could be used with two eyes and in December of the same year he announced he that had completed the production of what was certainly one of the world's first binoculars.

There was good and bad news for Lippershey. Although the binocular apparently passed inspection, with two more incorporating quartz crystal being ordered, the patent was denied on the grounds that such an instrument was already known to other parties. Nevertheless, Lippershey's skills were recognised by those in power and he was appointed telescope maker to the State of Zeeland.

WHAT IS A BINOCULAR?

A Galilean binocular

In simple terms, a **binocular** is an optical and mechanical device that allows the user to use both eyes to see distant objects close up, in three dimensions. Binoculars are, therefore, really just two **telescopes** which are fixed together so they point at exactly the same place. They take their name from the human ability to perceive the world in three dimensions, owing to our so-called 'binocular vision'. The spacing of our eyes means that our brain is able to detect incoming rays of light from objects at slightly different angles, enabling us to judge distance.

Using binoculars enables people to gain a 40% advantage compared to telescopes, since with two sets of signals, the brain is able to reduce interference by averaging electrical messages,

thus making fainter, lower contrast objects visible.

Hidden behind this simple description, however, is the much more complicated science of optics – a whole field of study in itself which combines chemistry, physics and mathematics. Most binoculars keep their glass components protected inside tubes which tend to be made of metal, though more open arrangements are possible. Binoculars are, of course, much more than just objects made of metal and glass: designers also play a key role in making them function correctly, as well as ensuring they are ergonomically pleasing and attractive to look at.

There are two main types of binocular: those using solely glass **lenses** (such as binoculars designed along Galilean or

Keplerian principles) and those using lenses in combination with **prisms** (prismatic).

Prismatic binoculars are further commonly divided into two varieties on the basis of the type of prisms they use – **Porro** and **roof prism** models. There are in fact a whole host of specific prism types which are used inside binoculars, all with special names.

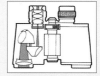

Porro prism binocular (left) and roof prism binocular (right) internal views

A Porro I binocular (left) and a Porro II binocular (right)

In 1609 the great Italian scientific pioneer and thinker Galileo Galilei (1564-1642) took advantage of the ideas of Lippershey by using a telescope modelled on his principles to explore the night sky, revolutionising the study of astronomy. The fame this brought to Galileo resulted in his name being given to the simplest form of binocular – the so-called 'Galilean' type which possesses a concave lens closest to the eye and a convex lens at the opposite end of the instrument. As well as using simple telescopes to open the world's eyes to the hidden wonders of the night sky, Galileo may also have dabbled with the manufacture of crude binoculars himself. In 1618 he is reported to have made a helmet with a twin telescope attachment for use at sea, though some authorities maintain that it has yet to be proven that this instrument used binocular principles. While simple binocular technology, therefore, was conquered by the second decade of the 17th century, it seems that very few instrument makers at this time were prepared to take on the challenge of producing correctly aligned binoculars that actually worked. There are only a

Porro prism binoculars can also be split into those of the **Porro I** and **Porro II** configurations.

In the last decade, a few large aperture astronomical binoculars have been made using mirrors in place of prisms and lenses.

Binoculars can be focussed using a central wheel which controls both eyepieces (**centre**

Some binoculars, like the Telescope Services 20x88 model pictured here, are huge, whereas others, such as the Nikon 7x15 instrument on top of it, are tiny

focus types) or by adjusting both eyepieces independently (**individual or eyepiece focus**). Occasionally, models appear that are of **fixed-focus** design, which are sharp from about 10 metres to infinity.

They vary in size from tiny instruments which easily nestle in the palm of a child's hand, up to huge devices which need to be mounted on a tripod or other sturdy base.

Binoculars are commonly described using two sets of numbers in combination (e.g. 8x30), the first indicating the magnification and the second referring to the diameter in millimetres of the objective lenses.

A **rangefinder** is a special type of binocular device which, as its name suggests, has a prime function of determining

the distance from a target to an observer. Rangefinders are used mainly by military personnel and have been described as the single most important and expensive military optical instrument prior to World War I.

An individual or eyepiece focus binocular (above) and a centre focus binocular (below)

handful of instruments in existence that date from this century, in comparison with many more telescopes.

The subsequent development of binoculars during the 17th and 18th centuries is marked by a series of innovations in optical design which, although mainly directed towards telescopes, in time would help to develop modern binoculars as we know them today. They began with the invention in 1611 of the inverting telescope by Johannes Kepler (1571-1630) which contained two just convex lenses and gave a wider and more uniformly-illuminated field of view than was previously possible. This was subsequently improved in the mid-1640s by Anton de Rheita (1597-1660), who re-inverted the image to produce what was called a 'terrestrial telescope'. Rheita's telescope also used more sophisticated 'compound' eyepieces, with the single convex lens being replaced by two spaced elements, thereby giving improved resolution and field of view.

Historical research suggests that the Capuchin monk Chérubin d'Orléans (1613-1697) played an important role in the development of binocular instruments during the latter part of the 17th century. Published works by Chérubin, dating from the 1670s and 1680s, present details of his extraordinary binoculars, with cardboard tubes of rectangular cross-section up to four metres long. There is even a later engraving showing three gentlemen appearing to use such an instrument for astronomical observation. In 1988 the Museum of the History of Science in Florence, Italy, displayed a four draw, metre-long ornamented cardboard binocular dating from the 17th century which was attributed to Chérubin. It may well be the oldest binocular preserved today and is thought to have been used by the appropriately-named Grand Duke Cosimo III of Medici.

Prismatic binoculars could be marketed in new and exciting ways to users familiar previously only with rather crude Galilean models. This 1898 advertisement from the French company Krauss shows the strong links between it and Zeiss that existed at this time. The images suggest both military and civilian uses of binoculars

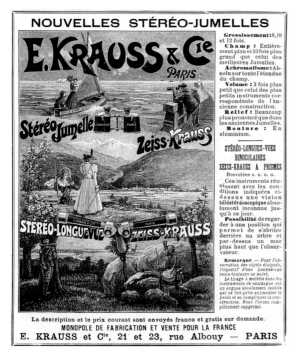

The problem of colour fringing in telescopes was addressed in the 1720s by combining lenses of different materials, and by the end of the 18th century Venetian optician Lorenzo Selva (1716-1790) would describe the use of a simple hinge arrangement in a binocular which could be adjusted to suit the distance between the observer's eyes. The availability of high quality optical glass was another challenge to be overcome. Although quartz crystal was a potentially viable alternative, it was more difficult to work than glass.

A key development was the incorporation of 'achromatic' objectives and eyepieces in binoculars, in which the individual lens elements were cemented together to reduce optical aberrations. The early pioneer of achromatic lenses had been Englishman

Chester Hall Moore (1703-1771), who developed them in about 1729. They were an important addition to binoculars because they reduced the amount of light reflected at air to glass surfaces, helping to produce bright images and cut down on unwanted internal reflections.

An important milestone came in 1823 with the launch of a simple Galilean instrument that was to lay the foundations for all opera glasses to come. Its pioneer was Viennese optician Johann Friedrich Voigtländer (1779-1859), who mounted two Galilean spy-glasses side by side, their extending eye tubes moving independently of each other for focussing. His design was adopted in Paris, where enterprising opticians refined the opera glass by the insertion of a stabilising bridge between the eye tubes and a central focussing mechanism.

By 1850 outdoor versions of the opera glass were being produced across Europe, often with higher magnifications (up to x6) and constructed more robustly than their indoor counterparts. Sometimes known as 'binocular field glasses', many of these instruments were given names suggestive of their potential uses – pilot glass, hunting glass and so on. Such innovations as extending range shades to keep out sunlight and rain, and loops for attaching neck straps were introduced as different manufacturers attempted to give their products an advantage over those of their rivals.

Galilean binoculars crossed the world to countries with people wealthy enough to afford these luxury instruments. This advertisement from a firm based in Calcultta, India, shows how Britain's colonial empire helped to bring binoculars to new horizons

A final development in the later decades of the 19th century was to see the manufacture of higher power binoculars for outdoor use, based on the principles of de Rheita. Known as 'deer-stalker's binoculars' or 'long Johns', they allowed magnifications of up to x20 to be achieved, while maintaining a wider field of view than their Galilean equivalents. Though much more expensive than opera glasses, they proved popular with certain user groups, despite their unwieldy length.

A giant leap forward

The most important leap forward in binocular design was arguably the introduction of prisms to simultaneously erect the image and fold the optical pathways into a smaller space. Its effect was so profound that over a century after Zeiss became the first company to produce a commercially successful prismatic binocular – which went on sale to the public in the early 1890s – this is still the principal type of construction.

Prisms are specially shaped pieces of glass with flat reflecting surfaces that, when used in binoculars, fold up the light paths, while still maintaining the magnifying power of the instrument. Capable of producing a correctly-aligned image in an instrument designed along Keplerian principles, they also provided the key breakthrough of allowing binocular tubes to be substantially shortened, while at the same time producing a wider angle of view than previous models.

The Italian engineer and inventor Ignazio Porro (1801-1875) was one of the first pioneers to recognise the value of prisms in optical devices, and gave his name to the most enduring of binocular designs. Thus we still have to this day the 'Porro prism' type of binoculars. His work on optics was influenced by his time spent surveying land during his years in service as an officer in the artillery corps. Although Porro had worked with Paris-based instrument makers to produce monoculars (one half of a binocular) using his prism erecting system (patented in 1854), neither he nor the various other companies experimenting with optical systems incorporating prisms, managed to make a commercial breakthrough. This is thought to have been due to the combination of low quality glass and unsophisticated optical production methods used at this time.

A few decades later in Germany the company of the late Carl Zeiss (1816-1888), the great optical pioneer, was granted an important patent in 1894 (pre-dated to 1893) for 'a double telescope with increased objective distance' (➤ page 19). These binoculars were based on the principles that Porro laid down, but were apparently produced without knowledge of the earlier work, and included the key innovation of having their objective lenses set further apart than their eyepieces. The commercial success of Zeiss's prism binocular allowed the company to dominate the binocular market until their patent expired in 1908. The Zeiss patent did not, however, stop several enterprising companies from producing prismatic binoculars with special designs that did not infringe the patent. Others, such as Bausch & Lomb in the USA, entered into agreements with Zeiss to distribute their binoculars overseas. When the patent finally expired, the rich variety of designs of competing companies began to disappear in favour of the Zeiss 'stereo prism' pattern, which became universal and set the mould for the majority of binoculars produced during the 20th century.

Further developments in prism design led to the emergence of new binocular types. The design impetus for many of these came from the need to circumvent the Zeiss patent. The company of another German optical pioneer, Moritz Carl Hensoldt (1821-1903), built on earlier breakthroughs with the development of binoculars incorporating a pentagonal prism system with a roof reflector which gave binoculars a more streamlined look. This resulted in the production, by

BINOCULAR MILESTONES

1609	1823	1854	1894	1898
Dutch eyeglass maker Hans Lippershey applies for a patent for his first simple telescope	Johann Friedrich Voigtländer produces the first modern-style handheld Galilean binocular	Italian Ignazio Porro receives a patent for his prism erecting system, which is used to make the first prismatic monocular	German instrument company Zeiss granted a patent for the world's first successful prismatic binocular (back dated to 1893)	Moritz Carl Hensoldt patents the world's first binocular with roof prisms, which became available in the Dialyt binocular range in 1905
	c.1729 Englishman Chester Hall Moore invents achromatic lenses			

Hensoldt, of the first 'roof prism' binoculars, patented in 1898 and available the following year. This was followed by the forerunner of the famous Zeiss Dialyt binocular, which became available from 1905. Most roof prism binoculars use the Abbe-Koenig system used in Hensoldt's binoculars, or the Schmidt-Pechan prism which was invented six years earlier. The sleek profile of these binoculars stems from the position of the objectives lenses which are roughly in line with the eyepieces. Although extremely innovative in their time, they would not see widespread uptake by binocular users until much later in the century.

Some of the first prismatic binoculars with objectives 35mm in diameter appeared in the UK in 1903. Produced by the Aitchison company, they were considered so revolutionary that they incorporated adjustable iris diaphragms to reduce light transmission during the day, thereby protecting the observer's eyes from strong sunlight. By 1910, however, Zeiss was to have introduced its first 7x50 binoculars. For the first time these instruments maximised the light-collecting properties of the fully dilated pupil, and they quickly became the standard configuration for night use.

While prisms brought what must have seemed like impressive wide angle views when they were introduced into binocular design in the late 19th century, the arrival of what we now think of as wide-angle binoculars followed some years later. Heinrich Erfle (1884-1923), yet another Zeiss employee, made this technological advance with a type of eyepiece that he developed in 1917 and still bears his name. Wide-angle binoculars were to bring many benefits on the battlefield as well as in civilian applications, and are still popular today.

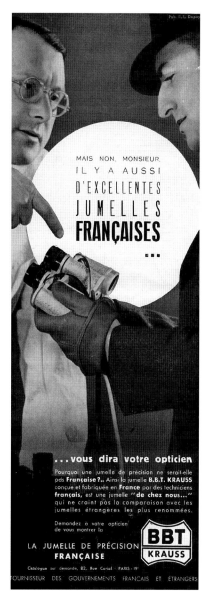

c.1919	1935	1958	1988	1990
The German company Goerz produces the Marine Nachtglas 10x56, the earliest wide-angle binocular	Zeiss employee Alexander Smakula pioneers the development of optical coatings to improve light transmission, with the Carl Zeiss T-coating	Binoculars with wide-field views for spectacle wearers introduced ('B-glasses')	Phase contrast coating developed to improve the performance of roof prism models	The first image stabilised binoculars are launched on the civilian market

THE ZEISS STORY

IT IS FAIR to say that there would not be much of a binocular story to tell were it not for the venerable company of Carl Zeiss Jena and its later offspring. This German optical giant profoundly influenced the direction of binocular manufacture with the launch of their 1894 prismatic models, still the blueprint for modern Porro prism binoculars.

A meeting of minds

We can tell the story of Zeiss today thanks to the pioneering efforts of three landmark figures in the development of optics. Chief among these was of course Carl Zeiss himself, who, as a youth was an apprentice in the small town of Jena at a company which made microscopes and scientific instruments. During this time he also studied at the local university where he apparently attended lectures on physics and optics – among other subjects. Quickly establishing considerable expertise in instrument design and repair, in 1846 Zeiss applied for and was granted permission by the Weimar authority to open a workshop of his own. He is reported to have sold just 23 microscopes in the first year of trading, but Zeiss's fledgling company expanded slowly as his high quality microscopes became more popular. A key milestone came in 1861 with Zeiss being awarded a gold medal at the Thuringian Industrial Exhibition, which was followed up by critical acclaim for the company's compound microscopes.

The optical pioneer Carl Zeiss, a key figure in the history of binoculars

The success of the company during this early period can be attributed to the first systematic use of rigorous optical design principles. Before this time optical design had been something of a trial and error process – more a craft than a science. Zeiss further enhanced the company's technical reputation by hiring a brilliant young university lecturer from Jena, Ernst Abbe (1840-1905), who laid out the framework for what would become the future of optical design. Abbe was to become a vital partner to Zeiss in pioneering the manufacture of high quality optics, forming a partnership in 1866 that would see Abbe become the director of research at the Zeiss Optical Works.

Despite the brilliance of the optical designs being pioneered by Abbe, no optical instrument could be fully effective without the use of high quality glass. Otto Schott (1851-1935), genius of glass production and another graduate of Jena University, was to provide the expertise that would finally allow the Zeiss company to produce its first successful binoculars. Aware of Abbe's work with optics, Schott wrote to him in 1879 enclosing a sample of his glass. Soon, Schott too would join the Zeiss company in an important collaboration in Jena to produce top quality optical glass.

Success with prisms

Although Schott's team produced the glass that would provide crystal clear binocular viewing

A German tobacco card from 1932 featuring Ernst Abbe, the great pioneer of modern binocular design. This card was issued by the German firm Zigarettenfabrik Yramos as part of a set entitled 'Inventors and Inventions'

late in the 1870s, the vital technological breakthrough had actually come seven years earlier. Ernst Abbe had independently invented the image erecting prism, which had already been conceived by Italian Ignazio Porro almost two decades earlier. The subsequent production of high quality crown glass by Schott at last allowed Abbe to use his prisms to create and patent the world's first successful prismatic binocular for Zeiss in 1893, which entered mass production the following year. Its key advantage, which enabled Zeiss to gain the patent, was to position the objective lenses further apart than the eyepieces, thus improving the three dimensional effect of the binocular.

The first Zeiss prismatic binoculars were give the name 'Feldstecher', which translates as 'field piercer', and the patent

lodged by Zeiss in 1893 also included details of other prismatic systems. These included a very distinctive binocular instrument, known as the 'Relieffernrohr', with objectives fixed well above the plane of the oculars. Later to become known as the battery commander's telescope or 'donkey ear' binocular, this innovative instrument allowed the observation of a target from behind a protective shield or from a trench (➤ page 40).

Zeiss's breakthrough prismatic binoculars proved popular, and the optical quality of these early instruments still impresses engineers over a century after they were first created. In the very early years only a handful of

varieties were made, building on the success of the 4x11 and 6x15 and 8x20 models of the initial launch in January 1894. Soon, customers were demanding new models and by the beginning of World War I Zeiss had developed almost 60 different types of handheld binoculars for civilian and military use.

An early 8x20 binocular from Carl Zeiss Jena, which features cursive script on the prism plates, which was used before the introduction of the more familiar logo. This example was made around 1900

In times of war

Although Zeiss binoculars were a status symbol for those people wealthy enough to afford them, they found an eager audience in the theatre of war. Throughout two world wars Zeiss constantly innovated in order to give Germany an advantage during times of conflict. Many Zeiss models could be fitted with range-finding graticules (➤ see page 34) ready for the demands of war and some of the finest ever binoculars were made during this period. These include models such as the now near-mythical 7x50 and 8x60 models used on U-boats and ships, which are so sought-after by collectors today. Many military binoculars from this period are found with the special three letter code 'blc' for Zeiss, which

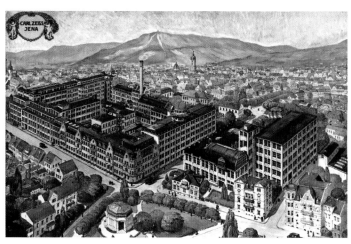

The Zeiss Jena works in 1910 showing the special viewing tower from where binoculars would have been tested

THE ZEISS STORY *continued*

the German strategic planners used in an attempt to keep the manufacturing locations of its optics secret from the enemy.

A key milestone for Zeiss came during World War II. Although the Jena factory largely escaped the effects of the Allied bombs, the German defeat inflicted great change on the company. It resulted in two separate divisions of Zeiss, one on either side of the Iron Curtain: Zeiss Jena in the Soviet-controlled east and Zeiss West in the quadrant of the country controlled by the Americans. War reparations also resulted in many of Zeiss's assets being distributed to other countries, further fragmenting the company. Some of the senior staff from Jena were relocated (sometimes against their will) to the American-controlled part of Germany, where the new division of Zeiss was to be set up. In turn, some German machinery, technology and even optical technicians from Jena were transferred into Russia where 'new' models soon emerged. Russian-made binoculars constructed

A Russian 8x30 post-war binocular, clearly based on the Zeiss pre-war Deltrentis design

after 1945 continue to surface which are clearly based on pre-war Zeiss designs.

The post war years

Production of binoculars in Jena apparently restarted rather soon after the end of the war. By contrast it took until 1954 for Zeiss West – now based in Oberkochen – to launch its new and ground-breaking 8x30 Porro prism model, which incorporated two lens elements separated by air, further reducing the length of the binocular and improving its image quality. Later innovations in the west quickly followed, included the sealing of civilian Porro prism models against humidity and moisture (1956) and the use of special designs to produce wide-field views for spectacle wearers (the so-called 'B glasses', 1958). Following Zeiss's acquisition of Hensoldt, which finally became complete in 1968, the Dialyt range marketed by Zeiss West became a global leader among roof prism designs, and was especially popular with birdwatchers and hunters. It was clear that throughout this period Zeiss West was benefiting from the intellectual and market freedom that its geographical location conferred on it.

Back in Jena, little new research and development was taking place, especially in the field

With the world's most advanced binoculars Only Carl Zeiss Western German binoculars with the patented trlo-objective system, 6-element eyepieces, internal rubber sealing and wi models for spectacle-wearers ■ Each Zeiss binocular in the range of seven different models is outstanding in it performance and between them they satisfy the requirements of the most fastidious and expert user ■ Descriptive booklet and name of your nearest stockist will be sent on request to the sole importers Degenhardt & Co Ltd 20/22 Mortimer St London W1

The Zeiss West 8x30, the first binocular to emerge from the newly westernised division of the company

of civilian binoculars. This may have been partly as a result of the low demand for binoculars in a country whose people had more pressing economic concerns to deal with. While some investment was put into the production of some excellent new military models – such as the DF and EDF 7x40 binoculars – technological stagnation was evident through the lack of new civilian models.

Some advances were, however, shared by both parts of the company, such as the use of anti-reflection coated lenses, which had been a military secret following invention in 1935. The first use of anti-reflection coating appears to have taken place at the Thomas Cooke Company in York in England in the first years of the 20th century, but that process was based on a chemical staining of the optical surfaces and was only ever an experimental novelty. The vacuum deposition of anti-reflection coatings developed by Zeiss was a real breakthrough, and rapidly developed into a productionised process. It brought huge benefits in terms of light transmission and in Jena gave a new lease of life to what were now rather dated optical designs. Despite their age, tried and tested models such as the 8x30, 7x50 and 10x50 proved very popular with users beyond the shadow of the Iron Curtain (➤ page 120). With the company hungry for foreign currency their highly competitive prices meant that they were readily snapped up by buyers, notably in the UK, other parts of Europe and in North America. By the end of the 1970s, when the prevailing economic situation in East Germany had improved, some excellent new civilian binoculars did appear from Zeiss Jena, such as the Nobilem Porro prism models and the roof prism Notarem designs.

Although hope remained that the two divisions of Zeiss might finally be unified, competition between the two companies gathered pace and led to some acrimonious disputes. These often centred on the use of the Zeiss name. A court case in the early 1970s resulted in the firm based in the West being granted exclusive rights to use the 'Zeiss' brand name in the USA. Instead, products made in the East were

to be renamed 'aus Jena', which surely had an impact on sales now that the respected Zeiss moniker had been dropped.

Eventually, with the fall of the Berlin Wall and the dismantling of the Iron Curtain, Carl Zeiss Jena produced its last binoculars, but some of its technology lived on – in spirit at least – by virtue of a new name in German optics, Docter, which bought the Zeiss Jena binocular assets in 1991 and produced a range of binoculars in Jena until about 1995. This leaves the Carl Zeiss Jena football team, which play their games at the Ernst Abbe stadium in the town, as the only living reminder of the illustrious optical past of this part of Germany.

A reunification of sorts was achieved by 1990 as small parts of the Jena-based company were 'cherry picked' by the Zeiss West executives. This would see some lens production continue at the former Zeiss factory in Jena. Though eager to benefit from the best minds working at Jena and the more profitable parts of the company, they were keen to avoid the huge financial liabilities of what was considered a largely inefficient operation by the standards of the West. Indeed, it took until 1996 for the unified Zeiss to finally make a profit.

A future without Jena

The final chapter in the Zeiss story sees the company continuing

to innovate in order to keep its brand at the cutting edge, with more recent developments such as a phase-contrast coating system (1988) which improved the performance of roof prism binoculars. This coating gets around a fundamental difficulty with all such prisms, whereby the fine detail of the images is slightly blurred, but with the new phase coatings this defect is completely corrected. The company, whose Wetzlar-based Sports Optics division remains a major player in the high end of binocular production, carries on the tradition begun by its founding fathers through the introduction of state-of-the-art models. The latest must-have model for all those with a love of fine optics is the FL roof prism range, which incorporates special fluoride-containing glass to reduce chromatic aberration (colour fringing). With such innovation the Zeiss name stands every chance of living on for another hundred years.

The Ernst Abbe Stadium, home to Carl Zeiss Jena Football Club, and a 21st century reminder of the vital role this east German town played in the history of binoculars

Advertisements
for Galilean
binoculars from
the 1950s showed
that there must
still have been
a market for
these simple
instruments over
fifty years after
the invention
of prismatic
binoculars

The many design breakthroughs and impressive range of binoculars offered by Zeiss ensured that the company had become a household name across much of the world by 1920. Its prominent position as a manufacturer of high quality binoculars during the first half of the 20th century stemmed partly from marketing efforts to portray Germany as the centre for binocular excellence globally. Other German-based companies such as Leitz and Goerz also benefited from such marketing, which ignored the fact that some high quality binoculars were also emerging from other European nations at this time – notably Austria, France and the UK. Indeed, contemporary advertisements show attempts by marketeers from non-German companies to suggest that they too were capable of producing instruments that could hold their own on a world stage. This is also borne out by tests carried out by the author showing, for example, that early prismatic 6x30 or 8x30 binoculars made outside Germany are actually capable of outperforming equivalent models made within its borders. This holds true for military as well as civilian models.

Further technological breakthroughs

The first half of the 20th century saw several manufacturers direct their efforts towards weight reduction in binoculars. Models that were previously formed substantially of brass were made lighter by the use of special materials such as aluminium in their construction. Other companies were preoccupied by making binoculars more resilient, improving light transmission or achieving distortion-free optical correctness. A final group focussed on adapting their instruments to special applications.

By World War I, special naval binoculars had been introduced using a special form of prism system which had been described by Abbe and before him Porro – the Porro II configuration. The demands of two world wars provided an important impetus for new binoculars with special features to appear, as well as leading to a huge increase in the numbers of standard instruments being manufactured in the countries affected by war. Some of the most impressive binoculars ever made were produced for the war effort, with landmark optical achievements such as the extreme wide-angle Deltar 8x40 binocular, produced by Zeiss in 1937, with an 80° apparent field. The demand for such a wide-angle binocular had come from World War I, when there had been an urgent need to detect attacking aircraft.

'The unnatural nature of vision through a monocular telescope leads to a falling off in efficiency over extended periods of observation. Apart from the effect of distraction resulting from vision by the unaided eye, or the effort involved in keeping it closed, the chance of seeing a target through a monocular is reduced by the statistical nature of vision and the presence of the blind spot. Telescopes used for exhaustive or difficult tasks, should therefore be binocular.'

BINOCULARS VERSUS MONOCULARS, A BRITISH MILITARY PUBLICATION

The British company Ross was the first to cement together prisms with one of the ocular lenses to reduce the number of air to glass surfaces and thus improve light transmission. It did this in its binoculars of the Porro II configuration, which show a step change in brightness compared to their predecessors. The use of optical coatings was, however, perhaps the most important technological milestone for binoculars during the 20th century. The process was pioneered by another Zeiss employee, Alexander Smakula (1900-1983), who invented the anti-reflective T-star coating which his company used to reduce reflections on air to glass surfaces. These were first patented in 1935. Microscopically thin chemical layers – typically of magnesium fluoride – have the unusual effect of actually *increasing* the amount of light transmitted through lenses and prisms. Building on the landmark work of Smakula, optical designers using today's state-of-the-art multicoatings have brought light transmission above 95%, a figure unheard of during the days of uncoated binoculars when 50% seemed impressive.

After the war

In the immediate years after World War II many manufacturers needed a period of adjustment as they once again tried to serve the needs of the civilian market. In Germany it took some years before the major companies were again to offer

BRITISH BINOCULARS

TODAY'S STUDENTS OF economic geography are sometimes surprised to learn that at one time the UK was a major force in binocular manufacture, with several high profile companies producing models that crossed the world.

Some of the most unusual and innovative models in the collections of binocular enthusiasts were in fact made by early British makers, such as Aitchison (who later merged with Dollond) who produced some important early designs. One of the more extraordinary of these was the unique aluminium folding binoculars that were used during the Second Boer War. (▶ page 32)

Major players

Although many firms tried their hand at binocular production, there were some heavyweight players in the British optical industry during the 20th century. They included Barr & Stroud,

Dollond, Kershaw, Ross, Watson and Wray. All these were built on the fine tradition of engineering that had helped the UK to become such as major global force by the start of the 20th century.

The major British binocular manufacturers also played a key part in the theatre of war, providing optical munitions to the armed forces on land, at sea and in the air. It is reported that the Leeds-based firm of Kershaw employed a large workforce of female employees in their factory towards the end of World War I in order to keep up with the demand for binoculars. This was an early attempt at the 'mass production' of binoculars using mainly unskilled labour and the firm is reported to have produced approximately 250,000 binoculars during World War II.

In his book *We're Certainly Not Afraid of Zeiss*, William Reid tells the fascinating story of Barr & Stroud and its attempts to take on the German optical giants in producing the best all-purpose naval binoculars. There is no doubt that the company's 7x50 model – which used the Porro prism II configuration – was able to compete with the best hand-held models that were coming out of Zeiss or Leitz in the war years.

Some landmark military binoculars from British manufacturers appeared during World War II, with surely the most

The Ross 5x40 air surveillance binocular

charismatic being the Ross 5x40 – a wide-angle, fixed-focus air surveillance model that would still be in service three decades later, despite competition from overseas suppliers. Some optical dinosaurs also emerged from British production lines during the war years, such as the 2.5x50 model used by pilots and for night use. This was the last British military binocular that used the prism-less Galilean optical arrangement.

Marketing efforts gather pace

British firms made efforts to market their binoculars overseas, sometimes to good effect, and some models can still be found in the exotic homes of users whose ancestors chose British. Many of the models sold overseas proved popular with the ex-pat community,

KERSHAW'S BINOCULARS

The modern Kershaw Binocular is an instrument of precision. The optical units are computed by mathematicians and the binocular is made throughout by specialised craftsmen. The foregoing, together with rigid inspection at every stage of manufacture, achieve for the Kershaw Binocular the proud position of "The World's Standard of Quality." A Kershaw glass will last a lifetime

There Is a Kershaw British Binocular to suit every purpose and pocket. If you have any difficulty in deciding which model to choose we shall be pleased to advise. Prices, including leather case,

from **£6/12/-**

Order from your dealer or write for illustrated list to

SOHO LIMITED, 3, SOHO SQUARE, LONDON, W.1
Member Scientific Instrument Manufacturers Association of Great Britain

The last British Galilean military binocular, with its finely crafted leather case

who no doubt felt more at home with their hands on a British-made instrument. Markets were also established in continental Europe, where there was a growing customer base for optics.

In the post war years British-made binoculars remained popular with domestic users. While some buyers took advantage of surplus military stocks, which were available at attractive prices in the immediate years after the war, others chose civilian models suited to a particular pastime. Some high quality binoculars were produced in the UK during this time. They include the Ross Stepruva 9x35 – a well proportioned wide-angle model that found favour among birdwatchers and boasts perhaps the best optical performance of any post-war British civilian binocular. Wray went further by marketing binoculars directly at the

birdwatching community, taking advertisements in the magazine *British Birds*.

British binoculars RIP

By 1980, however, binoculars for civilian use would no longer be made in the UK. The British binocular industry became a victim of the cheaper production methods and more innovative outlook of firms based in the Far East, principally Japan. Although a few military models continued to be produced by specialist makers such as Avimo, the production on British soil of these instruments too would soon be stopped.

While this is not the place to delve in detail into the history of binocular production on the opposite side of the Atlantic, it is interesting to note here that the American binocular industry suffered a similar fate to that which afflicted the UK. Bausch & Lomb, a company with a long and distinguished history of producing

Technicians at work on British binoculars in the workshops of Charles Frank, Glasgow in the 1960s

high quality binoculars, would see its last US-made binocular roll off the production lines in the 1960s.

Collecting British

Now that binoculars are no longer produced in the UK, a number of the noteworthy models manufactured by British firms have become sought after by collectors. The extreme wide-angle Ross 6x30 Stepnac and the evocative Kershaw Vanguard models are good examples of such binoculars. Other enthusiasts specialise in amassing a collection of all binoculars produced by a particular manufacturer. Although binoculars seem unlikely to be produced in the UK again given the prevailing economic conditions, the memory of such instruments is kept alive by those who collect, use and treasure instruments made in their home country.

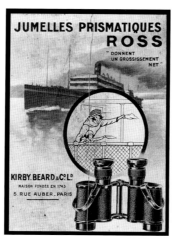

A 1920 advertisement for Ross prismatic binoculars from a French periodical. Such publicity illustrates the growing appeal of British-made binocular to buyers overseas

models for the civilian market, and there would never be such a varied range as had been available in the pre-war years. Further east, Japan proved to be a late developer in the field of binoculars, as discussed later in this chapter.

Although military surplus instruments could be obtained in large numbers following the end of hostilities, binoculars remained expensive to buy, even more so if they were centre focus models designed for civilian use. In the USA they even attracted a 'luxury tax' of 20% that was also applied to furs and jewellery. The main breakthrough did not come until the late 1950s and 1960s, when production in Japan became highly organised. This began a period of domination in many countries by affordable Japanese-made binoculars. It also saw the demise of several British and American manufacturers, who could simply not remain competitive or failed to introduce the innovations that would ensure their products caught the eye of consumers. Zoom binoculars also first appeared in the 1960s, and although proving popular for some users, are not generally considered to offer acceptable optical performance at high magnifications, despite their marketing hype.

Although China has been producing military binoculars since the late 1930s, it was during the 1990s that this country finally emerged as a major force in binocular production. While the quality of production of binoculars coming out of China varies very widely, this rapidly-developing economic powerhouse is clearly capable of producing some formidable binoculars. The best value models are those that use state-of-the-art production techniques, while still benefiting from the lower wages payable to workers in this massive country. Some commentators believe that China will soon become the dominant country in binocular production, with models to rival the very best from Japan, Germany and Austria.

In spite of these geographical changes Europe – or more precisely Germany and Austria – remains a key centre for binocular production, providing the bases for three of the 'big four' manufacturers in the shape of Leica, Zeiss and Swarovski. No-one could deny that Germany also stands alone as the spiritual centre for binoculars.

'In 1981, when Zeiss chose to issue a limited collector's edition of their 10x50 Porro prism model (discontinued in 1969), they were also making a statement that Porro prisms were a thing of the past, and that roof prisms were the de facto standard.'
                                                    ED HUFF & RENZE DE VRIES

Recent innovations

While night vision binoculars are not a new concept – early models having been used during World War II – the latest advances afforded by the current generation of night vision devices make viewing clearly in the pitch dark perfectly possible. In order to gain a competitive edge, other binocular manufacturers have attempted to add special features to their binoculars, often taking advantage of new technologies.

THE RISE OF JAPANESE BINOCULARS

DESPITE THE COMPARATIVELY late entry of Japan into the world of binocular production, by the end of the 20th century this nation would be producing some of the finest optical instruments the world had ever seen. What could explain the sudden rise to success?

Foreign dependency

Despite having its own optical research laboratory in Tokyo and fledgling binocular firms such as Fuji Brothers, at the beginning of World War I Japan's armed forces appear to have been almost entirely dependant on overseas suppliers of optical instruments. Inevitably, this supply dried up as hostilities continued, since the supplier countries suspended their exports of many products, including optical instruments.

Concern over this dependency on imports sparked Japan into action. By 1915 the country had already started efforts to produce its own optical glass and optical munitions through the setting up of new research and production facilities by the Imperial Japanese Navy. These efforts culminated in the formation in 1917 of a new company called Nippon Kogaku K.K. – the forerunner of Nikon – which was formed through the amalgamation of three smaller firms. As early as 1918 the company exported over 15,000 high quality prism binoculars to England, France, the USA and Russia. Basing many of its early projects on German designs, in 1919 the company went further by inviting eight German engineers to work for the emerging firm on five year contracts. This allowed the company to take advantage of German manufacturing processes, paralleling the successful optical firms of Leitz and Zeiss.

Boom and bust

In the years that followed World War I Japan continued to work tirelessly towards the goal of self-sufficiency in critical materials. During this time some landmark binoculars appeared from the Nippon Kogaku factory, including the tiny Mikron models that are still made today. Production of precision optical instruments such as telescopes, binoculars and rangefinders continued at Nippon Kogaku until the Great Kanto earthquake of 1923. In recognition of the company's vital importance in supplying optical instruments to the Japanese navy, its naval ministry arranged without delay for the reconstruction and reorganisation of Nippon Kogaku.

Despite experiencing financial difficulty in the years that followed – in part due to the slowdown in naval construction following the Washington Naval Conference of 1921 – the company survived as a key military supplier and an affiliated research arm of the Japanese navy. Certain optical munitions may have actually *increased* in their importance during this time, since special devices needed to be developed to give the Japanese navy tactical advantage in the face of limitations to overall tonnage brought by the various non-proliferation treaties of the 1920s. Other companies, such as Fuji, also aided the war effort during these critical years through the production of huge quantities of optical glass.

The challenges for Japan's optical industry nevertheless continued, and during World War II the country's optical works became the target of US air raids, with the plants of Nippon Kogagu and Fuji both being hit.

The key influence of the navy

There seems little doubt that both the financial and motivational support of the Imperial Japanese Navy for research and design was the key factor in Japan's eventual technological progress in the field of optical engineering. There is also much evidence to suggest that Japan's subsequent optical achievements were rooted in demands made by the military for specialized optical munitions prior to and during World War II. These included rangefinders and binocular periscopes.

THE RISE OF JAPANESE BINOCULARS *continued*

Post-war innovations

The investment in optical munitions by the Japanese navy laid the foundation for Japan's post-war optical industry, allowing emerging companies to take advantage of designs that had previously been produced solely for use by the country's armed forces. In addition to the early use of optical coatings, a further three additional factors contributed to the success of the Japanese optical industry after World War II: the production of prisms for rangefinders and periscopes; the successful mass production of binoculars; and the integration of optics with electronics and mechanical devices.

Following the war production of binoculars was begun by Nippon Kogaku as early as April 1946.

> 'As soon as the deck was awash, the order was given to open the conning-tower hatch and the yeoman of signals who was standing by, opened up and climbed onto the bridge. He was followed by the navigator. I myself was watching through the night periscope…at that moment the navigator shouted, "Bearing red nine-zero degrees, a possible enemy ship." I lowered the periscope, made for the bridge, and turned my binoculars in the direction indicated by the navigator. Without doubt there was a black spot which was clearly visible on the horizon in the rays of the moon.'
>
> Mochitsura Hashimoto, commander of the Japanese submarine I-58, shortly before it launched the torpedoes that were to sink the USS Indianapolis in 1945, with the loss of over 800 lives.

American servicemen occupying Japan became some of the company's most eager customers, thanks in part to the memory that Japanese military binoculars were some of the most prized trophy items for US naval officers. The experience that the company had gained in times of war enabled the emerging Nikon company to conquer initial difficulties and initiate production of high quality optics in a relatively short time frame.

Japanese design innovations soon began to be noticed outside the country. For example, sophisticated optical coatings on Nikon's photographic lenses after the war allowed them to outperform German-made models. In 1958 the company's reputation was confirmed by its camera and lenses being awarded the Grand Prix gold, silver and bronze prizes at the 1958 World Expo in Brussels.

The pioneering US optical company set up by David Bushnell turned to Japan in the 1950s to supply its binoculars, which were readily snapped up by customers who had witnessed a shortage of such instruments before, during and after the war. Bushnell found the accommodating attitude of Japanese binocular manufacturers to be the key to their success during this period, helping to make cut-price instruments of good optical quality widely available in North America.

By the mid-1950s the Nikon company had already launched a coated 8x30 binocular with similar performance to the very best models emerging from Europe. Two decades later, when the production of civilian Porro prism models by Leitz and Zeiss West was finally stopped, Nikon could rightly claim to be producing the world's finest Porro prism binoculars, an accolade it can still boast to this day (▶ page 65). Only the high quality Nobilem series, introduced by Zeiss Jena around 1980, could compete with the superb

A 1950s 8x30 binocular made by Nikon but also bearing the markings of Nippon Kogaku. This model provided optical quality on a par with the best binoculars being made in Europe at this time

binoculars coming out of Japan. The success of Nikon and other Japanese optical companies following World War II also sounded the death-knell for the British optical industry and led to the relocation to Japan of much US binocular production. Many firms could simply not keep up with the low production costs and technological advances taking place in Japan.

Some very special binoculars appeared in the 1960s and 1970s which were designed and made in Japan, including the wide-angle Swift Audubon 8.5x44, which many enthusiasts regard as one of the high points of post-war binocular innovation (◆ page 88).

Japanese binoculars today

The events described above have helped Japan to become a world leader in the production of high quality binoculars in the 21st century. Models by such companies as Nikon and Fujinon regularly top the polls among users and have a fearsome reputation for quality. The country does, however, now have a new rival in the production of high quality Asian-made binoculars in the form of its ever-developing neighbour China. This emerging super-power may well soon be producing its own optics that shock the world, like those made in the 1950s in the Land of the Rising Sun.

A Nikon HG L 8x32, a state-of-the-art roof prism binocular made in Japan

Leica was the first company to produce a binocular which incorporated an internal LED laser range-finding device in the form of its Geovid range, which appeared in 2004. At the touch of the button this provides a digital readout in metres showing the distance of the object in the middle of the field of view. Leica captured a significant new segment of the market with its Geovid binocular – which proved especially popular with hunters – and other major companies brought out parallel products following intensive research and development programmes.

Binoculars incorporating cameras have been in existence almost as long as binoculars themselves, but even the very latest digital models by such companies as Meade or Bushnell do not really perform either job especially well. Other offerings, such as binoculars with built-in radios, are really only marketing gimmicks.

A recent development sees the use of so-called 'hydrophobic' coatings to binocular lenses. These repel water and so make binoculars easier to use in wet conditions. Although Zeiss and Swarovski has made much marketing fuss over their new hydrophobic coatings – even giving them special trademarked names – they have apparently been used in Pentax binoculars for some years.

The latest chapter of binocular design comes in the form of image stabilised models. These, at the touch of a button, make viewing perfectly steady through the use of electronic and mechanical adjustments to the prisms. Although crude models have been available to military forces for some time, versions for civilian use first appeared in 1990. The models produced by Canon are perhaps the most successful of this new breed of binoculars, and allow users to see more and further than has ever been possible before with a handheld binocular (◆ page 74). The spectacular viewing effects made possible with stabilised binoculars would have surely impressed Ernst Abbe, the father of the prismatic binocular, and surely point to a new way forward as binocular production enters its fifth century.

2 Military service

'EYES ON THE HORIZON – His eyes glued to his binoculars, A U.S. Coast Guard lookout aboard a Coast Guard combat transport somewhere in the Pacific, watches for the periscope of an enemy submarine, the stacks of an enemy warship, or the wings of an enemy plane. With the lookout device, the lookout can immediately give the exact location of any foe craft he spots.'

These vivid words bring to life an evocative American photograph from World War II showing a young lookout at work. They capture the wartime sense of foreboding, as well as showing how special tools are needed during times of conflict to give armed forces a key advantage. This chapter explores the use of binoculars during war, stressing the human side of the story. Featured in the chapter are the stories of binoculars that have seen conflict in the major war zones, and the people who have used them or come to own them. The chapter also tells of special, vastly expensive binoculars produced by governments convinced that no cost should be spared to warn of the advancing enemy. It goes on to consider the desirability of certain military binoculars for modern day collectors, some of which can change hands today for enormous sums of money.

An atmospheric photograph depicting a binocular at work in war. The caption, written by the US coastguard publicity department, is given at the top of the page

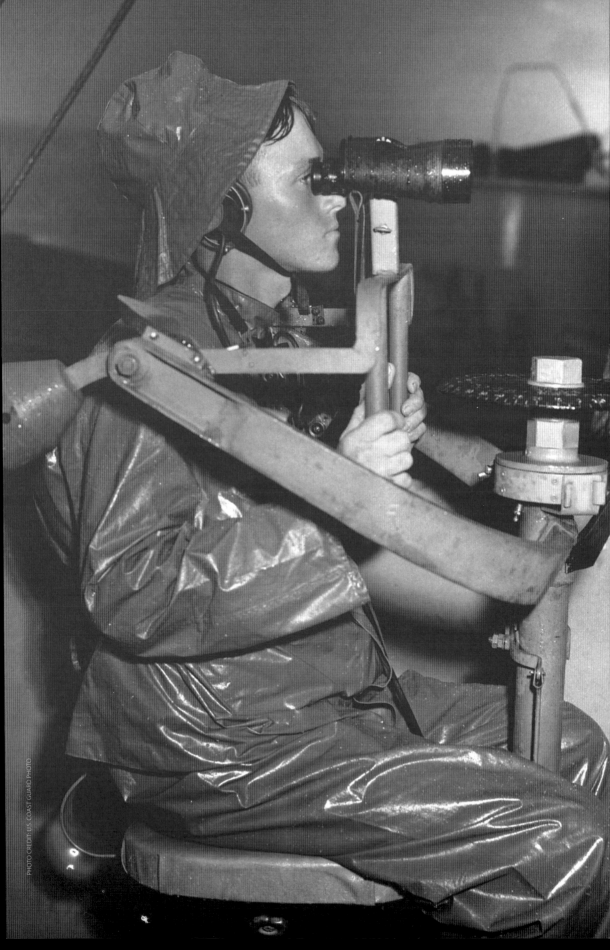

BINOCULARS HAVE PLAYED a more significant part in war than most people realise. Their ability to make the enemy visible, even at a considerable distance, meant that they probably found their niche in conflict zones soon after being invented. The stereoscopic properties of the binocular, which allow the user to make range estimates of targets, have helped to ensure that these instruments have taken their place in the theatre of war alongside other optical devices such as telescopes and periscopes.

Systematic use of binoculars by fighting forces most likely began during the American Civil War (1861-1865), with specially marked binoculars and contemporary illustrations from this period bearing witness to their use in that epic struggle. It was perhaps during this bloody conflict that the tradition began for leading military figures from the period to be pictured in uniform, complete with their binoculars.

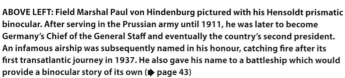

ABOVE LEFT: Field Marshal Paul von Hindenburg pictured with his Hensoldt prismatic binocular. After serving in the Prussian army until 1911, he was later to become Germany's Chief of the General Staff and eventually the country's second president. An infamous airship was subsequently named in his honour, catching fire after its first transatlantic journey in 1937. He also gave his name to a battleship which would provide a binocular story of its own (➧ page 43)

ABOVE MIDDLE: Colonel John Sedgwick, pictured with his Galilean binocular during the American Civil War. Sedgwick was a union army general and was killed by a Confederate sharp shooter at the Battle of Spotsylvania Court House in 1864. Expressing concern that his men were cowering in the face of a group of sharpshooters about 1,000 yards away, he is reported to have said the following shortly before falling to his death with a bullet hole in his eye – 'I'm ashamed of you, dodging that way. They couldn't hit an elephant at this distance'. Galilean binoculars were made for the U.S. Naval Observatory in tiny numbers during the American Civil War, but none of these instruments is currently known to exist. Should an example ever surface, it would be sure to be the find of a lifetime

ABOVE RIGHT: A Russian officer pictured with his Galilean binocular

RIGHT: A brightly-clothed and mounted Austrian officer pictured with his Galilean binocular in a postcard from 1912

BELOW RIGHT: The unique folding Galilean binocular that saw action in southern Africa during the Second Boer War

A simple Galilean binocular used by the British Army in World War I. The inset shows the 'crowfoot' admiralty marking, indicating it was accepted for use by the armed forces. Many of these early Galilean military binoculars were made in France

It is believed that superior German naval binoculars gave U-boats an advantage during times of conflict

In southern Africa three decades later, detachments of troops were equipped with a special folding binocular for use in the Second Boer War (1899-1902), although these may not have been part of an official government consignment and other makes and models saw action in this conflict. This innovative aluminium model, made by British firm Aitchison, was called the 'Aitchison pocket binocular field glass'. Although using simple Galilean lenses, it employed a complicated folding mechanism and remains highly collectable to this day. The demands of this war led to a huge increase in binocular sales to the British armed forces from the factories of Goerz in Berlin and Zeiss in Jena, and optical munitions made up over half their total exports to the UK.

For over a century and a half, therefore, binoculars have been part of the standard kit of the armed forces. In the UK the Ministry of Munitions even had a whole section devoted to the production of optical devices during World War I. Substantial investment in high quality military optics was seen as essential by many nations to give troops an advantage in times of war. There were tangible benefits – for example the outstanding performance of certain German naval binoculars during World War I and II is considered by some historians to have given that nation a distinct advantage during operations at sea.

The eyes of advantage

The prime purpose of binoculars in times of war is to sight the enemy and keep track of their position, whether they are on foot, mounted on a horse or in a vehicle or on board an aeroplane or ship. Binoculars also have a range of other specialist military uses, showing they are a versatile tool in times of war (◗ see box).

Photographs of World War II soldiers equipped with binoculars are testament to the importance of such instruments during the major conflicts of the 20th century

MULTIPLE USES FOR MILITARY BINOCULARS

Binoculars have a very wide range of military uses, as the following examples illustrate

'The chances are great that the lookout will be the first to observe danger. A faint wisp of smoke on the horizon may be the first indication of an approaching enemy surface unit. A single flash of sunlight on a wingtip may be the only notice of approaching enemy aircraft that can attack at a speed of 500 yards per second. A split-second glimpse of a periscope may be the only warning of an impending submarine attack. Failure to see a mere pinpoint of light on the horizon may mean that a buoy has been missed and a ship is grounded.'

US Navy Lookout Training Manual (2000)

IMAGE: US COAST GUARD

Shipboard lookout

Binoculars have provided the essential eyes for navies for generations. During military conflicts, lookouts play a critical role in acquiring visual contacts which can mean the difference between life and death for those on board. Even though sophisticated radar and other electronic equipment is now available to modern fighting forces, binoculars are still an important tool on board ships, sometimes providing the first sign of an approaching enemy. Radars and other electronic devices cannot distinguish between friend and enemy, hence binoculars are still useful. Special scanning tactics – such as the 'step-by-step' method – have been developed to ensure that no portion of the ocean or sky is ignored.

Coastal defence

Throughout much of World War II a key element of the British war effort was directed towards keeping constant watch over the country's vulnerable coastline. Thousands of observers were stationed at vantage-points, especially along the English Channel, working in tandem with military personnel operating primitive radars and listening devices to detect incoming enemy aircraft.

Artillery

While the rangefinder was developed as a specialist type of binocular device to provide the accurate determination of distance, binoculars have long played an important part in estimating the ranges of targets for artillery units. This is one of the reasons why range-finding graticules (scales inscribed on ocular lens elements and visible when looking through the binocular) are a standard feature of all military binoculars. Before such graticules were routinely incorporated into the lens elements of binoculars, some early devices used calcite windows to help observers determine distance, often with helpful scales displayed on the binocular casings.

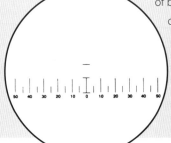

The view through a binocular fitted with a range-finding graticule

An early Huet range-finding binocular from about 1905. The calcite window is introduced into the field of view by turning the milled wheel in the right eyepiece

Searching for submarines from the air

Special binoculars have been developed that help to detect the tiny signs that a dangerous submarine may be just below the surface. King among these was surely the Sard 6x42, an extreme wide-angle binocular commissioned by the US government during World War II and used for aerial observation of the sea (as well as being used on board ships and on land; ▶ page 37). Over sixty years after being used in combat, this amazing x6 wide-field binocular has never been bettered.

A World War II US navy binocular blinker attached to a 7x50 binocular

Sending and receiving of signals

Before the widespread use of high quality prismatic binoculars, a special non-prismatic instrument incorporating the Kepler lens configuration was used by the British navy to receive signals at sea. Although its image was inverted the high light transmission helped the observer to pick out signals over long distances and in dim lighting conditions. In World War II, a 'binocular blinker' device was developed by the American navy for the sending and receiving of morse code signals at sea. It consisted of a special battery-powered device that sent a narrow beam of light to a second observer stationed some distance away. A cloaking grill ensured that unwanted observers did not also see the signal.

Search and rescue missions

Finding sailors lost at sea following battles that saw ships sunk or damaged was an important activity for certain air-based military personnel. They used binoculars of low power and good light gathering ability (such as 7x50 models) to make observations while sweeping vast areas of ocean.

Searchlight direction

The use of searchlights was an important line of defence during World War II. Binoculars were often used to sight targets, with observers providing directions to the operators of the huge lights that would illuminate aircraft to make attack from ground-based guns easier. These binocular observers sometimes even took control of the devices themselves. Some models of binocular were developed specifically for this purpose, such as the low power, wide-angle x4 model of Porro II configuration produced by British firm Ross.

Night use

In Britain the Royal Air Force employed low power 2.5x50 Galilean binoculars for night-time use as

MULTIPLE USES FOR MILITARY BINOCULARS *Continued*

part of airborne operations in World War II. These instruments, which were uncoated but incorporated large objective lenses, are sometimes still found with their original leather cases, providing evidence of their specialist use (▶ page 24).

Ship spacing

Binoculars incorporating laser range-finding devices are used by those on board naval vessels while steaming at sea in order to help keep the correct distance between ships.

Aircraft identification and target acquisition

The impressive German 10x80 binoculars of World War II were designed specifically to help to identify enemy aircraft over the skies of Europe. Made by a

variety of companies, these very sturdy binoculars were mounted on special tripods and cowlings that allowed observers to pinpoint the bearing and elevation of potential targets. Three examples of the large 12x60 binocular made by Zeiss were also mounted on a gigantic 4-metre height and rangefinder to determine such variables.

IMAGE: US COAST GUARD

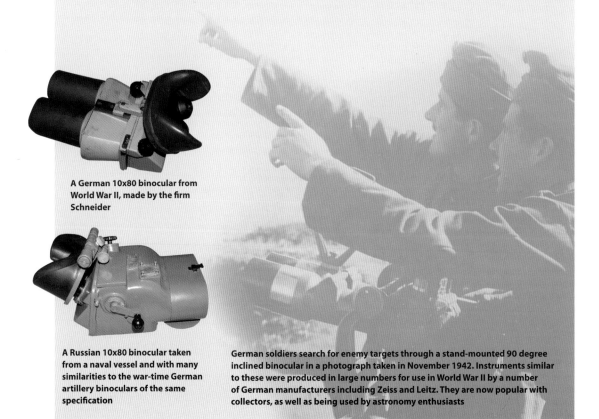

A German 10x80 binocular from World War II, made by the firm Schneider

A Russian 10x80 binocular taken from a naval vessel and with many similarities to the war-time German artillery binoculars of the same specification

German soldiers search for enemy targets through a stand-mounted 90 degree inclined binocular in a photograph taken in November 1942. Instruments similar to these were produced in large numbers for use in World War II by a number of German manufacturers including Zeiss and Leitz. They are now popular with collectors, as well as being used by astronomy enthusiasts

BINOCULAR WITH A HISTORY

Zeppelin binoculars?

THIS GOERZ X12 'Trieder Binocle' comes with a fascinating past. It was reputedly taken from the wreckage of the Zeppelin airship that crashed at Cuffley, Hertfordshir e, while attempting to raid London in WWI. A teenage boy, among the first on the scene next morning, found the

binocular and kept it until his death in the late 1970s. The binocular came with a rather tatty case with the letters 'W' and 'R' inscribed on it in capitals. Its magnificent condition, coupled with the wonderful history of the binocular, resulted in it fetching over £300 in an eBay auction in 2007.

LANDMARK BINOCULAR: THE SARD 6x42

The finest handheld binocular ever?

WHILE NOVICE BINOCULAR users find looking through many models a little fiddly, the Sard 6x42 has been known to evoke shrieks of joy from those who place their eyes to this binocular for the first time! This is surely a major contender for the best handheld binocular ever made.

The Sard 6x42 allows such natural wide-angle views that using it is not like looking through a binocular at all – it is like holding up a huge round window six times closer to the world. This binocular produces views that are truly unique at x6 magnification and quite unlike any other model in history.

This special binocular owes its existence to the conflicts of World War II. Used principally by the Americans for airborne submarine spotting, this binocular was also used at sea and on land for aircraft observation. The Sard 6x42 is a chunky binocular which could never be described as lightweight and a special mounting device was available to take its weight when used at sea.

In use it is the amazingly comfortable wide-angle view that is most striking. While some observers have to try very hard to see the full field of view in other wide-angle models, in the Sard the full 70 degree apparent field is immediately obvious. Experienced users liken its picture to the relaxed

view possible through the revered German 8x60 and 10x80 war time binoculars.

The Sard 6x42 was made by the Kollsman instrument division of the Square-D company in Flushing Meadow, New York. At least two Sard 7x50 models were also made, but these were conventional models without exceptionally wide fields.

The exquisite performance of the Sard 6x42 puts into that rare band of used binoculars that will fetch over £500 in good condition, and mint examples have been known to go for closer to £1,000. It remains scarce, but can be found on US eBay in very small numbers.

Another US-made World War II binocular, the Bausch & Lomb Mark 41 7x50, is perhaps the only other non-German binocular which might be considered for the title of the best handheld model ever. Its tiny production, however, means that it is very rarely encountered and its prices are now astronomical.

TECHNICAL SPECIFICATION

SARD 6X42
Field of view: 12° (212 m at 1,000 m)
Apparent field: 70°
Exit pupil diameter: 7 mm
Weight: 1712 g

A variety of highly specialised models have been produced for military purposes, including some of the finest models ever made in terms of optical performance, since the demands of war meant that huge budgets could be put into their development. The extensive use of binoculars during military operations has also led to the development of a range of accessories and auxiliary devices to improve their functionality in times of conflict.

One example of a special device to improve the efficiency of binocular observation in the theatre of war is the Royal Air Force's 'holder for binoculars', a British device made of brass, felt and leather that allows the user to rest his arms on a cross brace while the binocular itself rests on a support. The instruction manual for this device states that it is 'designed to improve and assist observation and to facilitate scanning with binoculars in aircraft'. Its use apparently eliminated fatigue on the arms and permitted steady observation, even in bumpy flying conditions, over long periods.

The accompanying manual also includes instructive photographs showing how the holder for binoculars could be used on board aircraft in various positions by the observer. When seated, the base of the holder could be rested on the lap or on the seat between the observer's legs. When standing, the weight of the holder and binoculars was taken by the lanyard on the observer's shoulders.

Binocular scanning with the holder was reported in the manual to considerably increase the efficiency of visual searching on anti-U-boat and air/sea rescue patrols, because binoculars can be used with the holder continuously, without effort. It suggests that the average range of pick-up of U-boats with the naked eye was about five miles, but that scanning with binoculars increased that range by half as much again in normal visibility and even more when visibility was good. When searching for snorkels or dinghies, binocular viewing was said to give a three-fold increase in the range of pick-up because of the smaller size of the objects.

Training in binocular use for service personnel is clearly important in order to get the best out of such instruments. As well as issuing instruction manuals, many of which are unfortunately still classified documents, some armed forces produced instructional films that were designed to educate large numbers of people in one sitting. One example is the four-minute US navy film in the lookout training series entitled 'binoculars'. It features helpful basic guidance on using and caring for such instruments, stressing that the binocular is the most important piece of equipment issued to lookouts. The US navy must have been especially concerned about damage to binoculars

A 1944 advertisement heralding the arrival of 'the first waterproof binocular'. Such material helped to bolster the reputation of major companies such as Bausch & Lomb, who turned over much of its production to military binoculars in the war years. The final paragraph optimistically looks ahead to a time when Americans could enjoy new breakthroughs in binocular design, once the war was won

Binoculars Like This Must Pass a "Swimming" Test

Bausch & Lomb developed the first waterproof binocular—a binocular which can be immersed in a tank of water, yet due to its water-tight construction, not a drop of water can get into the interior to log the optics or interfere with its perfect functioning.

This engineering achievement required a complete redesign of the instrument, complete re-tooling and revised manufacturing

procedure. All this was accomplished without interrupting the scheduled even flow of needed binoculars to the armed forces.

Based on this redesign, both the Army and Navy now specify that *all* binoculars supplied to them be of waterproof construction.

Facilities of this plant—developed through 90 years of service to outdoor enthusiasts, to science and industry—are busy today fighting a war. After Victory new

miracles of optical science for better living will come from the drafting tables, the glass furnaces and the precision finishing rooms of Bausch & Lomb, optical headquarters of America.

BAUSCH & LOMB
OPTICAL CO.   ROCHESTER, N.Y.
ESTABLISHED 1853

AN AMERICAN SCIENTIFIC INSTITUTION PRODUCING OPTICAL GLASS AND INSTRUMENTS FOR MILITARY USE, EDUCATION, RESEARCH, INDUSTRY AND EYESIGHT CORRECTION

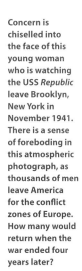

Concern is chiselled into the face of this young woman who is watching the USS *Republic* leave Brooklyn, New York in November 1941. There is a sense of foreboding in this atmospheric photograph, as thousands of men leave America for the conflict zones of Europe. How many would return when the war ended four years later?

Binoculars proved especially useful during war time artillery operations. Here, postcards show the use of binoculars by French (left) and German (right) forces

caused by careless use, since the following warning is contained twice in the film – 'Keep that neck strap around your neck where it belongs!'.

Most military binoculars are of the eyepiece focus design as these are easier to make waterproof and dustproof. Additionally, during war it is rarely necessary to focus on very close objects, so most users would simply set the focus once and the binocular would then be sharp from about 50 metres to infinity, without the need for further adjustment.

The use of slices of coloured glass as filters is particularly well developed in military binoculars. It is still quite common to find instruments from World War II complete with one or more sets of these filters, which fit snugly over the eyepieces. Yellow tinted filters seem to be the most commonly used; they help to cut through haze and on dull days can improve contrast and resolution. Green filters (cutting down glare at sea) and grey ones (reducing the effects of strong sunlight) are also frequently found. Some manufacturers used sophisticated mechanisms to enclose the filters within the housing of the binocular, such as those used in the well known British navy Barr & Stroud CF 41 7x50 model. More recently laser protection filters have been incorporated into military binoculars.

RIGHT: Donkey ear binoculars in use in World War I (top) and World War II (bottom). During World War I observers sometimes hid themselves inside 'fake' trees which contained a chamber within to allow a person to pass unnoticed. Images such as these will become increasingly important as the number of surviving veterans who served in these conflicts dwindles

FAR RIGHT: A 1979 advertisement for the periscopes of Barr & Stroud, a British company with a long history of supplying the navy with optical instruments

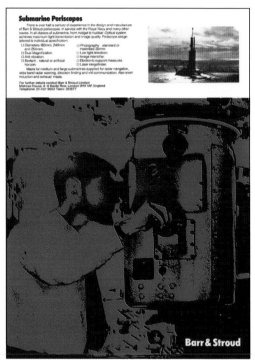

Among the more specialised binoculars produced for use during war are the distinctive periscopic 'donkey ear' or 'scissor binoculars' that were first used during World War I. These allow the user to observe from a hidden position, as well as gaining an impressive three-dimensional view of the battlefield owing to their increased objective separation, allowing distance to be estimated more easily.

'One of the great moments in my life was standing on the signal bridge and watching the signing of the surrender document through a pair of binoculars. I felt so proud to be part of the service.'

FILM ACTOR TONY CURTIS, COMMENTING ON HIS SERVICE AS A SIGNALMAN ON BOARD USS PROTEUS. CURTIS'S QUOTE REFERS TO HIS OBSERVATION OF GENERAL DOUGLAS MACARTHUR ON BOARD A CAPTURED JAPANESE SUBMARINE IN SEPTEMBER 1945

RIGHT: Although Japan is thought to have been a late developer in terms of its optical industry, by World War II hundreds of thousands of Japanese binoculars were in use at sea and on land. The text that accompanies the image far right states: 'If there is preparation, we are not afraid of the enemy'

BINOCULAR WITH A HISTORY

My Tirpitz Binoculars

IN THE AUTUMN of 1947 my father Angell Larsen was employed as leader of the navigations department and charts office with *SKN*, Sea Defence Commando Northern-Norway, based in Tromsø. His work involved the drawing and correcting of sea charts and the judging and calibrating of navigation equipment of a technical and optical nature, from compasses to binoculars. At the end of the war the Norwegian military took over all military equipment that the Nazi war machine left behind.

The famous battleship *Tirpitz*, pride of the German fleet, had been the target of endless allied attacks of varying success in both Kåfjord in Finmark county and Håkøybotn near Tromsø further south. On the 12 November 1944 Tirpitz was finally sunk by the RAF in Kvaløysundet, Tromsø, in a clear weather raid with no allied losses. However, it was during the course of repairs following one of the earlier Kåfjord raids that the German navy salvaged and systematically marked and listed all equipment lightly damaged and that could be put into use elsewhere. The day/night binoculars that I now own were part of a batch of navigational equipment from *Tirpitz*, marked lightly damaged and still giving a slightly diffused view in a section of the left ocular. They had been mostly used at night, permanently mounted outside on one of the two bridge wings.

The binoculars are a model made by Carl Zeiss in Jena for the Kriegsmarine (German navy); they are the rare D.F. 10 x 80 model with 20 degree inclined eyepieces. To the right of the eyepieces there is a plate engraved or embossed with initials and identifying numbers under the Kriegsmarine eagle. This plate is critical in establishing authenticity regarding time of manufacture and supply. The protective shades for the objective lenses are missing; these were hinged from the front brackets. The sighting piece is in place. As I was informed by my father they are not an infrared night vision device (or AFIK, only the Allies had deployed this) but rather an artillery binocular, with adjustments to determine the bearing or elevation of a target. The lever on the left (TAG) can insert a neutral or coloured filter for bright sun or other difficult viewing conditions, which can be removed for night use.

The binoculars were never used by the Norwegian navy and when the navigation department was moved to the NATO base at Ramsund near the Lofoten Islands in 1953 all the salvaged equipment went with them, including that from *Tirpitz*. After many years it was decided to dispose of the old items from the Second World War. My father considered it a waste to throw away 10 kg of quality Carl Zeiss optics and saved them from destruction. We have looked after them since, and following his death I have inherited them.

We eventually decided to sell them and they were sold on eBay in November 2007 for £1,500.

Marit Bøe Larsen

IMAGE: MARIT BØE LARSEN

The huge periscopes made for submarine use comprise a separate group of highly specialised binocular devices. These are in fact perhaps best termed 'binocular monoculars', since they tend to have just one objective lens, used in combination with one or two eyepieces. The use of an effective periscope while under the surface of the ocean is clearly a life and death issue

The Carl Zeiss Jena 7x40 DF – nicknamed the 'Checkpoint Charlie' binocular following its use in East Germany during the Cold War

for those entombed in the otherwise blind metal shell that constitutes a submarine. The British binocular manufacturer Barr & Stroud specialised in producing state-of-the-art submarine periscopes, with much marketing effort being directed towards gaining lucrative military contracts.

The most extraordinary military binocular ever developed was without doubt the gigantic instrument with 200mm objectives made by Carl Zeiss Jena. While the precise function of these leviathans is not clear, they may have been used to track the trajectories of outgoing missiles. Only three of these giants – which weighed in at over half a tonne when placed on their rock steady mounts – are thought to have been produced, no doubt at enormous expense to the German authorities. Their huge oculars provided what must still be unsurpassed viewing at x20 and x40 magnification. One of these binoculars is on permanent display in the Military Museum in Koblenz (➧ page 195), Germany, having been loaned from the USA where it found its way after the war.

'Every vessel shall at all times maintain a proper look-out by sight and hearing as well as by all available means appropriate in the prevailing circumstances and conditions so as to make a full appraisal of the situation and of the risk of collision'

US Navy Navigation Rule 5

The Fujinon 7x28 – a compact military binocular issued to US armed forces in the 1990s. The author sold such a binocular on eBay in 2008, which was bought by the father of an American servicemen to accompany his son to Iraq

Some models of military binocular will be forever linked to particular periods of history. For example, during the Cold War binoculars were used to help prevent citizens from East Germany fleeing the grip of Communism to the more prosperous world over the border. Perhaps the most famous model of this era was the so-called 'Checkpoint Charlie' binocular from Carl Zeiss Jena – the 7x40 DF or NVA. This high quality Porro prism binocular has attracted a mythology all of its own, and whether or not it was systematically used by border guards in that famous location in Berlin it was without doubt used by the East German authorities to survey the terrain along the Berlin Wall and other border zones. This model, and others such as the American M19 7x50 (used in Vietnam conflict) and the British Avimo 7x42 (used in the Falklands War) continue to be sought after by binocular enthusiasts today seeking a particular military connection.

Binoculars, like any artefact of war, have the potential to keep alive fascinating stories about their past, which are sometimes linked to landmark periods in our history. Several such binoculars with a history are celebrated in this book.

BINOCULAR WITH A HISTORY

The Zeiss 6x30 Hindenburg

I ONCE OWNED a unique little Zeiss 6x30 binocular which was salvaged from the wreck of the German Battlecruiser SMS *Hindenburg* which was scuttled at Scapa Flow, Scotland in 1919. The *Hindenburg* was the last capital ship to be scuttled and the only one raised upright. She settled on the bottom with her superstructure above water and was raised and broken at Rosyth Dockyard in Fife in the early 1930s.

The firm of Cox and Danks raised the scuttled vessels and formed a scrap consortium which became known as Metal Industries. Hiring the then mothballed naval base at Rosyth, they successfully raised and scrapped many of the scuttled High Seas Fleet, ironically using German tugs to bring them to Rosyth. My father remembers seeing some of these battleships being towed into the Firth of Forth, but he can only recall the upturned vessels with little huts on for the towing party. This practice was stopped when Hitler intervened, stating it was dishonourable for German tugs to tow German warships to be scrapped by the allied powers. During the dismantling process priority was given to armour plate and non-ferrous metals which may explain the loss of the brass objective rings on this particular binocular. Workers were allowed to take small sundry items, if permitted by a foreman, but not any non-ferrous material.

It was common practice to sell off items considered valuable. On arrival at Rosyth and before any breaking began, the ship was also opened to the public for a nominal fee and the money raised given to a local hospital. For instance, the letters making up the name of the ship the RSS *Mauretania* were auctioned off for £12 each and the internal fittings were also sold off. There are very few families in this area that didn't have

something off one of the ships broken at Rosyth or at Inverkeithing. I still have a White Star marked wooden coat hanger and much of the teak that my father used to make shelves was from the *Mauretania*.

If this binocular was in a fairly grubby state it's perfectly feasible that it was given away, particularly if the auction for any souvenirs had already been held. Despite this, the binocular seemed remarkably clear to view through and was a testament to the quality of Zeiss, Jena. Slight oxidation took place on the outside but, considering its origins, this binocular was in remarkable condition giving crisp, clear and collimated images with no damage, chips or fungus present.

Unfortunately, the engraving on the right prism plate suffered more than the left and no serial number could be seen – only the 6x30 designation. To have survived in such a fine condition, it must have been in a watertight locker or in the superstructure. The leather shows no sign of having been soaked and has not split.

I bought the binocular at a jumble sale years ago with a little label on it stating 'from the Hindenburg' but after all this time it's unlikely we'll ever know the name of the person who thought it worth keeping. All in all, this was a unique binocular with a fascinating history.

Niall McLaren

IMAGE: NIALL MCLAREN

Given the comparatively heavy weight of binoculars, especially for soldiers already burdened with large backpacks and a range of other equipment, it is perhaps surprising that governments have not invested more heavily in research into lighter, compact models. The introduction in the 1990s by the US military of the Fujinon 7x28 compact binocular for use in Iraq – complete with its sophisticated laser protection filters – appears to be one of the first examples of a truly compact waterproof model being a standard issue item to soldiers in a conflict zone.

'In July 1939 our holiday was spent on the Isle of Wight. There were very many warships in and near Southampton and Portsmouth. We stayed in pleasant accommodation not far from the beach and booked a beach hut for the duration of the stay. From the terrace we could watch warships practising techniques and planes landing on and taking off from aircraft carriers. My father's binoculars were in constant use. All of this was very frightening for me as I didn't really understand what was going on.' IAN BILLINGSEY

Supply and servicing

The importance of binoculars in war means that in many countries a comprehensive system is employed to obtain supplies and then distribute and service instruments. In the two great world wars, some armed forces supplied their officers or other ranks directly with binoculars, others – especially during World War I – provided a bursary that allowed binoculars to be purchased privately to be taken to war. It is still possible to find examples of essentially civilian instruments bearing the names of serving soldiers and their regiments.

Reconnaissance...VISION...DECISION

When sniper's bullets whip past your head — when you have to send your precious few tanks and men into the teeth of enemy machine gun and artillery fire — that's when good vision counts! When every decision is influenced by *what you see*—your field glasses become an important instrument of warfare.

Military field glasses need more than the ordinary measure of precision in magnification and field of view. Their value is only as great as their light gathering power.

VARD is making lenses, prisms and reticles for our Army and Navy. With skill born of tradition in making precision equipment,

VARD technicians work on these optical parts knowing that only *perfection* is *good enough*.

Other VARD divisions produce navigation instruments, aircraft hydraulic parts and actuating units, precision testing equipment and precision tools for machined parts. The hope and earnest effort of VARD management and men together is to give our soldiers, sailors, marines and airmen the tools which can win —tools that are the *best* that can be built — Anywhere.

VARD INC.

PASADENA, CALIFORNIA

BINOCULARS WITH A HISTORY

Two world wars

This 1917-issued British-made Dollond Royal Navy 6x30 binocular was used by a father in World War I and by his son in World War II.

Active service

This US-made 1942 naval binocular was recently found in a barn at the edge of the Hutgen forest in Belgium. Fierce and costly fighting in the densely-wooded area occurred at the end of 1944. For some reason, the binocular was used as a hammer as both objectives were smashed. Such binoculars set one to wonder what terrible circumstances might have led the previous owner to mistreating the binocular in this way. The binocular has been restored to its former glory by the current owner.

Saved by a binocular?

This 1939 Russian army binocular was damaged by a bullet, but continued in service following its repair. It may have been made in Germany as Russia received military aid in return for allowing German artillery testing, prior to World War II.

Serving two countries

Two Zeiss military binoculars, used by the Germans in World War I, brought home as souvenirs and later donated to the British war effort in World War II. They are marked with the special military arrow or 'crowfoot' marks to signify acceptance into military service. The right hand binocular is a 1917 navy 'marineglas' and to the left is a pre-World War I army glass.

Finding your way

A very early military Galilean binocular complete with a fully working compass marked in the traditional German manner, with an O for Ost (east). Some later military and marine binoculars would feature an in-built compass, visible through the binocular when in use.

In distinguished company

A binocular belonging to Major General Archibald Graham Wavell who commanded the British 15th Brigade during the Second Boer War. He came from a family of soldiers, with his father serving during the Peninsular Wars against Napoleon and his son commanding the 30,000 British Commonwealth Forces in Libya's Western Desert in World War II. The binocular was made in London by the instrument maker and optician Jacob Pillischer.

The importance of binoculars led to the production of literally millions of examples during the major conflicts of the 20th century, with lucrative contracts given to the companies that could be most competitive. A 1920 binocular advertisement from Bausch & Lomb stated that the company was then supplying more than twice as many binoculars in a week for military purposes than it formerly did in a year.

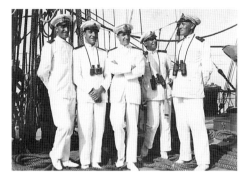

During both world wars, however, some countries struggled to supply the quantity of binoculars needed by those in conflict zones. This led, on both sides of the Atlantic, for public appeals for binoculars to be loaned to the armed forces. Optimistically, there was sometimes also the offer of the return of the binocular after the end of war.

Italian navy personnel pose on the deck of their ship. Their binoculars (which look like Zeiss 6x30 and 7x50 models) stand out against their immaculately clean uniforms

A most curious story surrounds the attempts by Britain to supply the quantities of binoculars it needed during World War I. It has been reported in several sources that, using Switzerland as an intermediary, the British government negotiated a deal with Germany in 1915 for the supply of binoculars (and telescopic sights) in return for rubber, of which the Germans were apparently desperately short. It seems that some 30,000 binoculars were ready for immediate delivery. While the deal never went ahead, perhaps because the Ministry of Supply's efforts to boost home production of binoculars finally began to bear fruit, this episode shows the lengths to which the British government was prepared to go in order to supply its armed forces with the optical munitions it needed in times of war.

'In June/July, I was taken prisoner of war and handed to the Italians by the Germans. I was taken with only the clothes I wore and a fine pair of binoculars which I had to trade with the Italian soldiers for water to drink.'

ARTHUR JOHNSONE, RECALLING HIS JOURNEY TO THE INFAMOUS
BENGHAZI PRISONER OF WAR CAMP IN LIBYA

Although binoculars have long been recognised as important optical aids during times of war, systematic tests to determine the best configurations and models appear to have been a late arrival. During the early months of World War II the US navy carried out tests which determined that a 7x50 was the best binocular for night-time use, closely followed by the 6x30. The British armed forces went further by carrying out exhaustive tests of binoculars from a variety of makers, before awarding substantial contracts to a variety of British manufacturers – notably Barr & Stroud, Ross and Kershaw.

The equipment servicing departments of armed forces have long used the skills of technicians to keep instruments such as binoculars in tip-top shape. A 1941 British manual details no less than nine different types of tests, including the formidable 'rough usage test' (➤ page 51).

BINOCULARS WITH A HISTORY

Cold War booty

THE BINOCULAR PICTURED came with a fascinating oral history. It was previously owned by a member of the Royal Corps of Transport, who was a driver for senior military personnel. He was working in East Germany a few days before the fall of the Berlin Wall, and arrived at an East German barracks. His senior officers discovered it was a divisional headquarters with, among other things, 300 'Stalin' tanks. The senior German officer confided in his British counterpart that only 45 were operational, since the remainder had been cannibalised to run the others.

It also turned out that the East German Lt. Colonels were living five to a room and carrying out duties of Guard Commander, a situation that would have produced apoplexy among British forces. One of the soldiers, who were all desperate for foreign currency and perhaps knew that the Berlin Wall would soon be breached, sold his Russian-made 7x50 binocular to the driver who brought them back to the UK on his return. He said that he regretted not having some more money with him, because there also were some impressive-looking optics on the tanks!

Distinguished history

THE BARR & STROUD binoculars pictured have lived through a varied and even distinguished history over the last sixty or seventy years. They were a vital tool of Lt/Cdr. Walter Mears, DSC RNVR during the Normandy landings in July 1944, when he was navigating officer on a flotilla of gun boats. The binoculars had already been part of his equipment in mine-laying operations out of the Kyle of Lochalsh, in the waters around Iceland, and on decoy duties with Arctic convoys. But it was during the capture of Walcheren Island, in the Netherlands, in November 1944, that they proved their worth. With no navigational marks remaining, and the flotilla's progress hampered by swift and dangerous tides, the binoculars had many

souls depending on their efficiency in aiding a successful capture.

After the war, Lt/Cdr. Mears restored a minesweeper to its former state as a charter yacht in the Mediterranean. He sailed for three years without incident around the Greek Islands, with the help of his faithful binoculars. In 1950, the binoculars emigrated (with their owner) to Africa, game-viewing and bird-watching in Gorongosa, Wankie and Kruger game reserves, while the owner settled in Rhodesia.

When Walter Mears died, he left his precious binoculars to his son, who lives on the west coast of Scotland. Now retired, the binoculars spend too much time shut away in the dark, superseded by lighter, smarter, clearer models. But occasionally they are brought out to show some patient watcher the seals, basking sharks, dolphins and gannets passing by.

Lt/Cdr. Mears received a DSC, mainly for his part in the Walcheren operation; the old binoculars deserve more than a dusty cupboard.

Martin Mears

Despite key optical advances in the years following World War II, some binoculars dating from this period are still in service in the armed forces of major nations. For example, there are reliable reports of Ross 7x50 and Kershaw 6x30 models being used by the British army right into the 21st century. Such a finding is sure to fuel the belief that some military personnel are still not equipped with the state-of-the-art equipment that their dedication deserves.

Several binocular manufacturers used their military connections to add marketing gloss to their products following the war years. People were invited to consider that instruments whose performance had been tried and tested in the rugged conditions of war, also made the most sensible purchases for their own day to day use.

10 × 80 Ex-Admiralty Battleship Bridge Binoculars

The Admiralty commissioned Ross of London to produce a binocular which would have good penetrating and resolving power even under the dullest of lighting conditions. The resultant 10 × 80 binocular proved to be one of the finest tripod supported instruments ever to be produced. The instrument is fitted with internal filters which can be used to advantage in strong sunshine or in haze. This large binocular is 20" in length and weighs 18 lbs., and is supplied complete with extremely rigid metal tripod. Price complete—£75.00

'The Battle of Britain was becoming more intense, so with my mother, grandmother and sister, I was evacuated into Devon. We had the opportunity of becoming government evacuees and moving to Canada or the USA but the family decided to stay together. Grandpa handed over his precious binoculars and the iron railings at the school were given up to the war effort.' IAN BILLINGSEY

Collectors of British military binoculars today would be eager to pay just £75 for a pristine example of the legendary Ross 10x80 'battleship bridge' binocular. This advertisement comes from a Charles Frank catalogue of 1973

In the hands of collectors

The collectability of military binoculars has been touched on above, and a whole chapter of this book is later devoted to the broader topic of collecting. While the human story behind many military instruments may not have survived, numerous binoculars *have* been saved and many are eagerly collected. At the top end of the rarity scale, however, it is increasingly becoming a hobby for the wealthy. The price of some of the finest war-time binoculars continues

Gebetsandenken
an den
tugendsamen Jüngling
Georg Islinger
Gastwirtssohn von Walpersdorf
Oberfeldwebel in einem Inf.-Regt.
Inhaber des E. K. II, Infanterie-
Sturmabzeichens und Verwundeten-
abzeichens

welcher am 5. Oktober 1941 östlich Smolensk im Alter von 26 Jahren den Heldentod erlitten hat.

R. I. P.

Vorbei ist unser sehnend Hoffen,
In unserer Mitte Dich zu seh'n,
Das Schicksal hat uns hart betroffen,
Doch Hoffnung spricht:
Auf Wiederseh'n!
Mein Jesus Barmherzigkeit!
Barmherziger Jesus, gib ihm die
ewige Ruhe!

Druck Max Herzog, Rottenburg a. Laaber

'I love the army binoculars with their usurous magnification of vision.
The world has only two unfaded colours left:
The yellow of jealousy and the red of impatience.'

OSSIP MANDALSTAM

LEFT: This incredibly poignant photograph and text is reprinted from a German 'death card' of 1941, announcing the falling in action of Georg Islinger. It is a reminder of the terrible cost of war

to rise, with the 8x60 and 7x50 U-boat models now commanding many thousands of pounds.

Following World War II large numbers of British military binoculars were sold off to the general public through outlets such as London's Headquarter & General Supplies Ltd. Though most were the workhorse 6x30 and 7x50 models made by firms such as Kershaw and Ross, a few rather special models also appeared at knockdown prices for a limited period. These included the now scarce Ross 10x80 'battleship bridge' binocular, together with German Zeiss UDF 7x50 U-boat glasses that were presumably seized following the end of the war. The latter featured in a 1965 catalogue for the amazing price of £29 – only £11 more than the humble Ross 7x50. This prized German glass now changes hands for more than £1,000.

In the UK, a major annual militaria event called 'War and Peace' is probably the best place to find a wide range of ex-military binoculars. There are rumours that at the 2008 event a knowledgeable dealer paid another over £2,000 for a rare 'tall' 8x60 U-boat binocular in superb condition, only to sell it to a collector for £1,000 more when the gates were opened to the public the following day.

MY BINOCULAR STORY

Old is best

THE BINOCULARS I take in the car whenever I go on holiday belonged to my father's brother, who was an officer in the artillery during the First World War. He fought through the carnage and, ironically, died of influenza a few days after the Armistice in 1918. His binoculars – which he would have called 'field glasses' – were passed on to my father, and have been in my family as long as I can remember. They are solid brass, painted black and the body is covered with some sort of leatherette. There is a broad arrow (for the War Department) on the front, and on the eyepiece end is 'Binocular Prismatic No 2 Mk 1: Magnification 6: No. 5958, and on the other side is 'Ross, London,

1916', and the addition, 'Graticuled by Sherwood, London'. They weigh nearly 2 lb. and are still kept in their original heavy leather case with 'Hood J.W.' incised into the leather at the back.

God knows what grim sights my uncle must have seen through these during the war. Now they are used purely for pleasure, and particularly for bird-watching while on holiday. Each year I visit North Uist in the Outer Hebrides, and often sit on the machair above the beach at Balranald Bird Reserve with the innumerable waders and other sea birds scampering along the tide line. On one occasion I was walking on the machair, and came across a few people painting. 'Are those First War binoculars?' enquired an elderly lady, and when

I said they were she said, 'I've still got a pair like that – belonged to my late husband. His father took them off a dead German!' I assured her that mine were truly British, and went on my way.

I expect there are still many in existence, and in regular use. Many years ago I took them to London to be cleaned – probably to Negretti and Zamba – and the man said, 'I'll take out the graticule, as it's not necessary and is probably discoloured.' The result was, and is, brilliant magnification and pin-sharp images. You may keep your very expensive, super-compact, lightweight, plastic models. I shall stick to my 92-year-olds and, although I am in my mid-70s, hope to be using them for some time yet.
David Hood

Magistrate's decision

Harold Percy Smith (50), a clerk, of High Road, Chiswick, was sentenced to six months' imprisonment with hard labour on charges of stealing two binoculars, worth £32 10s, lent to Paddington Borough Council, and used by him when roof-spotting for the council in November and January last. Mr Stothert, prosecuting for the council, said that Smith pawned both glasses and went on duty with one of the empty binocular cases which he had retained. It was not until the owner of one of the binoculars asked for his one to be returned that the thefts were discovered.

THE TIMES NEWSPAPER, 16 JUNE 1941

Military binocular tests

Notes on Repairs to Fire Control Instruments
(Part 43: Prismatic binoculars and monoculars; issued in 1941 by the British Military College of Science) lists the following nine tests for binoculars that ordnance mechanical engineers and armament artificers might employ to keep these precision instruments in serviceable condition.

- Verticality of image
- Parallelism of optical axes
- Parallelism of binocular axes
- Definition test
- Equal magnification test
- Graticule testing
- Dioptre testing
- Interocular scale setting
- Rough usage test as follows:

Spray test: spray 10 minutes eyepieces upwards – moisture should not enter

Drop test: from 6 feet with eyepieces upwards, on to a box of silver sand 6 inches deep, covered with a thin cloth. Adjustment should remain correct.

Cord test: hang binoculars on a 10 feet cord by the hinge pillar, raise 6 feet and drop. Repeat with cord on each sling-holder. Adjustment should remain correct.

Heat test: raise to 120 degrees F at a rate below 20 degrees per hour, leave for 12 hours in dry or moist air. Grease should not melt or damage occur.

ABOVE: The cases that protected binoculars were also subject to tests. This example appears to be a sample sent for testing to the British Ministry of Supply's Directorate of Stores. Its label still bears the seal from 1953

LEFT: The importance of binoculars during times of war is apparent in the many toy soldiers which are depicted wearing these optical instruments

ABOVE: Military collectors have a special fascination for objects associated with the German expeditionary force in Libya and Egypt during the North Africa Campaign of World War II – known as the Afrikakorps. This card, featuring a solider using his 'desert-sand' painted binocular, is the first of four official cards depicting various armed forces and issued in 1942. The card is cancelled with a special postmark which was only used on 11 January but in 133 towns. The stamp is overprinted for use in the Ukraine

MY BINOCULAR STORY

A fair swap

JACK BEST, a hairdresser from Manchester, was enlisted into the Royal Navy in April 1941 as a Stoker (2nd Class) and given the service number 118706. He soon joined HMS *Penelope* as a 1st class Stoker and his ship subsequently saw action in the Mediterranean and the Far East.

While engaged in operations, HMS *Penelope* was asked to receive some captured German navy officers whose U-boat had been sunk. Never one to miss an opportunity, Jack – nicknamed Banjo by his fellow seamen – enquired of the officers if any of them might fancy a haircut. One officer seemed quite taken by the idea and asked if Jack would let him have some cigarettes too.

After the haircut was complete the German officer lent over to Jack and handed him a black leather case, stamped with the date 1944 and the markings of the German navy, containing his 7x50 binoculars.

Delighted to be given such an unusual object, Jack was happy to offer up some cigarettes to complete the swap. He was later wounded in action and returned to his home in northern England – complete with his unique memento of war. Thirty years on from this incident Jack still owned the binocular, and used to enjoy telling his grandchildren about his adventures during the war on the high seas. One of his grandsons was captivated by the fascinating story of the binoculars, and used to be allowed to look out of his bedroom window with them when staying with his grandpa. Perhaps it is not surprising that this little boy – whose name is Brin Best – grew up to have a lifelong passion for binoculars.

BB

7x50 binoculars made by the Czech company Srb and Stys for the German navy and given to Stoker Jack Best by a captured German submarine officer during World War II

A 1973 advertisement for British military surplus binoculars, showing that war time supplies were still being disposed of almost three decades after the end of hostilities

BINOCULAR WITH A HISTORY

A Dollond for three generations

PAMELA MCBIRNIE can trace her Dollond and Aitchison binocular back almost 100 years, spanning three generations of her family. The binocular, marked 'The standard 8x30', appears in a photograph that depicts her grandfather, Robert Edward White, which was taken around 1920. The broad arrow marks and military nomenclature on this particular model, however, suggests that it had been in use during World War I, most probably by Robert's son Albert. Albert joined up for service in 1917, travelling to, among other places, Sudan and Egypt.

Pamela remembers as a child her grandfather encouraging her to use binoculars, allowing her to become familiar with using them early in her life. Her grandfather used the Dollond for general purposes when outdoors in the countryside around his house. The binocular passed to Pamela's mother and eventually to Pamela herself. She has used it for birdwatching and also for watching passing ships on visits to the coast. It is now very much a treasured heirloom, and intertwined with the history of her family.

Robert Edward White with his Dollond 8x30 binocular

IMAGE: PAMELA MCBIRNIE

3 In the service of man

Binoculars are often thought of as tools to enhance people's quality of life – but they can also be tools to save lives. This chapter shows how dedicated people have used binoculars as part of their work at sea and on land to protect people from harm. It also explains how they are a vital tool for scientific research of various kinds, helping to make new and important discoveries that will set the world alight. The chapter also deals with the varied ways in which other professionals make use of binoculars in the course of their work. As you read this text, there is no doubt that somewhere in the world a vital observation will be taking place as binoculars are used in the service of humanity.

Binoculars help lifeguards to keep watch over busy beaches. Here, Lt. James Garland, (far right) a full-time City and County of Honolulu Ocean Safety lifeguard, uses his binoculars to scan the south shore of Oahu for any ocean goers in distress (photo by Michael De Nyse)

BINOCULARS HAVE A long association with the sea, and despite modern monitoring techniques they still play an important part in keeping safe people on board vessels at sea. The Royal National Lifeboat Institution (RNLI) is one example of a UK charity that uses binoculars to save lives on the ocean. Each year it rescues people who have got into difficulties in the country's coastal waters, and is one of the UK's most well supported charities. Every lifeboat is equipped with binoculars ready to help save lives.

The RNLI is aided in its work by Her Majesty's Coastguard (a government-funded service) and another, lesser known, charity – the National Coastwatch Institution. This organisation, run by volunteers, provides a visual watch along

A volunteer scans the ocean from the dramatically located NCI station at Bass Point, Cornwall. Here he uses a giant, tripod-mounted Russian 15x110 observation binocular to monitor the movements of small fishing vessels. The station watches over a 'no man's land' off the Lizard with no traffic separation zones

the coastline that has also saved lives. It was established in 1994 following the tragic deaths of two fishermen who drowned right below a recently closed coast-guard station in Cornwall. Unfortunately, most of the country's watch stations were closed following a period of rationalisation and modification. The charity originated out of a campaign to re-establish a visual watch for Cornwall and the first NCI station was opened in a dramatic cliff-top setting at Bass Point in 1994. An extensive refurbishment by volunteers was carried out, though when the station opened the team was there with its binoculars, even though there was no electricity, heating or toilet!

There are now 37 operational Coastwatch stations around the coastline of England and Wales, staffed by 1,600 voluntary watch-keepers. Binoculars are an essential part of the toolkit of these highly trained volunteers, who track boats and ensure that any vessel getting into difficulty is quickly provided with support from the appropriate authorities. As well as providing a watch in all weathers, watch-keepers monitor radio channels, radars, sea conditions and weather, and provide a listening watch in times of poor visibility. All volunteers are provided with extensive training, which includes visual observation techniques, marine chart-work and radio procedures. In one year alone 145 serious incidents reported by the charity ended with a call-out of the RNLI lifeboats, RAF Air Sea Rescue or other rescue agencies. Many hundreds of minor incidents were also dealt with by informing the coastguard of lost and found children, distressed marine wildlife and ordnance on beaches.

'If you had no means of communication and you were not SEEN, then who could help you?'

LYNN CURNOW, FORMER STATION MANAGER AT THE BASS POINT
NATIONAL COASTWATCH INSTITUTION STATION, CORNWALL

The binocular is one of the key tools in the armoury of land-based lifeguards too, who keep watch around our shores. The RNLI website gives details of the personal lifeguard kit, which includes 'tough, durable binoculars…designed with the beach environment in mind, allowing the lifeguard a closer look at a situation far away'. Lifeguards respond to medical emergencies on land and in the water, including incidents up to 300 metres out to sea. They patrol more than 70 beaches across the UK during the peak season.

Thousands of miles away in North Carolina, USA, a special binocular is helping land-based rescue services to find lost and injured people in remote parts of the Blue Ridge Mountains. The specialized instrument, which incorporates gyroscopic stabilization as well as a night vision facility, has been provided to the North Carolina Helicopter Search & Rescue Team by the U.S. Department of Homeland Security. The binocular removes vibrations from a helicopter or moving vehicle, providing the clear imaging that is critically important when searching for people. It can also be used during flood incidents, being capable of spotting a stranded person's head or arms projecting out of the water. The device will give the rescue services a major advantage in life and death situations and can be used in conjunction with a thermal camera to provide the ultimate search and rescue binocular. This dedicated North Carolina team comprises volunteer rescuers from several departments in the west of the state and is chartered to assist anywhere in North Carolina, as well as in the team's base in Transylvania County.

Keeping an eye on you

Binoculars are an important tool in covert surveillance and have featured in countless TV detective series and big screen films in that guise. The US company Bushnell mentioned in 1960s adverts the use in Vietnam of their 7x35 Rangemaster model by counter-intelligence personnel. UK police today are known to use binoculars for a variety of specialist uses. These include spotting trouble makers at football games and scanning with night-vision binoculars across areas of open land which are known to be frequented by thieves. A less conventional use of night-vision binoculars by law enforcement officers is their deployment to detect the heat plumes from the secret attic rooms where cannabis plants are being cultivated.

Using binoculars in public places can arouse suspicion. Somebody scanning across a park with a binocular today would be sure to raise a few eyebrows

This association with surveillance is perhaps the principal reason why using binoculars in urban areas tends to attract suspicion, unless the user is wearing some sort of official uniform. During the preparation of this book the author had reason to test hundreds of binoculars in the environs of the city of Leeds

where he works, and each time he ventured outside carrying binoculars he would sense that he too was being watched. In fact there were some areas of the city where he would certainly not have used binoculars at all for fear of getting himself into trouble with the local residents or authorities.

Exploration and scientific research

Binoculars continue to play a significant part in scientific surveys of various types, as they have done for many decades. Indeed, early binoculars sometimes come on the market bearing intriguing markings linked to explorers of the past (➡ see box).

The early exploration of Australia by Europeans is known to have taken advantage of the binocular as an instrument which can find life-giving water holes. On the key expeditions of John McDouall Stuart in 1861-62, whose team was the first to cross Australia

BINOCULAR WITH A HISTORY

Looking for fossil fish

THIS PRE-WORLD WAR I Watson x8 civilian binocular was used during scientific expeditions to Nyasaland (now Malawi) in the first decade of the 20th century. It is marked 'TEG Bailey', was fitted with a graticule and belonged to a geologist who explored the region between 1906 and 1909, publishing several scientific papers on the fossil fish remains he found there with A.E Andrew. Later, Bailey joined the army at the outbreak of World War I, won a military cross and was killed in action in Russia and is buried in the Archangel Allied Cemetery in that country.

IMAGE: NIALL MCLAREN

from south to north, Galilean binoculars and a telescope were used to spot green areas in the far distance which indicated the presence of water. This technique of 'navigation by water' allowed Stuart to progress safely across what would otherwise have been extremely hazardous terrain to traverse in the searing heat of this barren part of Australia. Stuart's binoculars survive to this day as an evocative museum exhibit.

Over a century later binoculars were still being used on expeditions to the far corners of the world. In 1982 a team headed by Dr Holger Dietz spent the Antarctic winter in Georg van Neumayer station in Atka Bay, accompanied by three binoculars – the 7x50, 8x56 and 15x60 models. With temperatures as low as minus 46°C, snow storms and dim light, this was a real test for binoculars. The team nevertheless found the instruments of tremendous help, as well as being a great pleasure to use.

A Zeiss binocular was part of the equipment of the first German Chamlang Expedition to Nepal in 1990, with the two principal climbers reaching the main 7,319-metre peak on 21 October in the company of their Zeiss 8x20B/GA binoculars. One of these climbers later went on record to say that his binocular had partly accounted for the successful completion of the

Zeiss used its association with explorers to give a rugged allure to its binoculars

expedition, allowing the team to make out changes in the ice crevices and cracks in the snow on the 2,000m-high north-west face of the mighty Chamlang.

Geological surveys to this day often make use of binoculars to study inaccessible rock exposures and to scan suitable terrain for further investigation. The author has seen a Carl Zeiss Jena 8x30 Jenoptem in use in the Pyrenees by a sedimentology professor studying the folded rock formations of this majestic mountain range.

ZEISS PRISM BINOCULARS

Zeiss Binoculars have become "standard equipment" with professional explorers, guides, navigators, etc. They are also the choice of that great army of outdoor Americans who are satisfied with nothing but the best.

At leading opticians', camera dealers', and sporting goods stores. Write to us for Catalogue.

CARL ZEISS INC
485-D FIFTH AVE., NEW YORK
Pacific Branch: 728 So. Hill St., Los Angeles, Cal.

MY BINOCULAR STORY

Fossil hunting

IN THE DAYS when I used to go fossil hunting on the south coast of the UK, I carried with me a German WWII dienstglas 6x30. This glass proved useful for scanning the cliff sides for the promising clay strata of the Jurassic period and for locating suitable and safe investigation sites. The graticule also proved valuable on occasions for helping estimate width and distance. The great advantage of the 6x30 was, of course, its relatively compact and lightweight nature, yet its image stability and not unreasonable magnification were advantages as well. In my view the typical military 6x30 (especially the lightweight ones) remains a first choice for this kind of amateur geological work. One should perhaps point out that taking a sturdy case for the binocular was essential, especially as some of the clay sites could be quite loose and slippy.

Geoffrey Samuel

Surveys of sea mammals and fishes are an example of binoculars being placed in the service of nature. Volunteers join with paid coordinators to conduct dolphin, whale and shark watches around the coastline of the British Isles. The principal sites include Cardigan Bay in Wales (known for its resident group of bottle-nosed dolphins) and the coast of Cornwall (where basking sharks gather in summer). During 2008 members of the public were asked to join a concerted effort to find out more about the basking sharks that spend the summer months around Cornwall's rocky coastline. The project, organised by the Cornwall Wildlife Trust, resulted in gruelling 12-hour watches being carried out at strategic locations across the county. Observers had the thrill of seeing, at close quarters, sharks bigger than great whites and capable of swallowing a person whole. The fact that basking sharks are in fact plankton feeders and harmless to humans only adds to their mystique. The hope is that the research can be used to put pressure on the government to declare marine conservation areas to protect these magnificent fishes.

> '*Through my binoculars I was allowed to enter the often hidden world of the dolphins as they rode the bow wave of the ship*' JARVIS HAYES

The rise of so-called 'citizen science' has allowed members of the public to use their binoculars to make important observations as part of mass participation surveys. The most well known of these in the UK is the Royal Society for the Protection of Birds' (RSPB) garden birdwatch project, which sees hundreds of thousands of people raise their binoculars to count the birds visiting their gardens every February. The author can provide evidence of the key importance of binoculars in bird survey work from his days as a marine ornithologist and there are many testimonies showing how they have been used for conservation projects overseas (➧ see boxes).

MY BINOCULAR STORY

Seabirds at sea

I SPENT A year as a marine ornithologist in the early 1990s counting seabirds from ships at sea as part of a research project organised by the Nature Conservancy Council – a former UK government agency. The project led to the production of atlases showing the distribution of birds at sea, which were used to assess conservation priorities and in case of oil spills.

The work demanded long hours and keen observing skills, as our job was to record in a standardised way the species of seabird seen as the ships steamed through UK waters. I worked on board ferries, fisheries research vessels and even a frigate of the British navy – HMS Anglesey.

The day started at dawn irrespective of the time of year and in northern Scotland that meant 3:00 am in summer! I would have a quick wash and some breakfast and then head out onto my vantage-point, usually on the bridge wing. At the start and end of each observing period we took latitude and longitude readings from the bridge, so that our observations could be placed in geographical context.

We used recording forms pinned to a clipboard and had to note details of the time of observation, which species we saw, their age (determined from their plumage) and the direction of travel if flying. For observation we used then state-of-the-art Zeiss 10x40 BGAT roof prism binoculars which certainly produced wonderful views of passing birds. When on the navy frigate my Zeiss binoculars caused a lot of interest, as on board they also used Zeiss binoculars – the rubber armoured 7x50 Porro prism model.

There were many wildlife highlights during the year, but it was a tough and lonely job too and a little boring at times. The day was very long in summer and it could be really monotonous counting gull after gull drifting around the boat and nothing else! I had to keep telling myself this was serious research because we were in uncharted waters in terms of our knowledge of seabirds at sea in UK waters.

A treasured memory was a trip in September into the South-west Approaches, an area of ocean beyond the Scilly Isles where the sea suddenly deepens as you approach the edge of the continental shelf. It was migration season and the ship steamed through an area where hundreds of petrels and shearwaters had congregated, many concentrated around trawlers. I was able to get close-up views of exotic species such as great and Cory's shearwaters, birds that had flown thousands of miles already and still had yet to complete their amazing migrations.

In the same area in May we encountered a plankton bloom and the sea went milky, with strange creatures such as sun fish and blue sharks sticking their fins out of the water. At one point, within an hour, two summer plumage Sabine's gulls and a stunning long-tailed skua flew overhead and I was able to study exquisite feather detail through the Zeiss binoculars.

Still to this day when I see a Zeiss 10x40 binocular, a model that is still popular with birdwatchers even though it is no longer made, it evokes those memorable days as a marine ornithologist as I did my bit to advance our knowledge on the distribution of seabirds.

BB

MY BINOCULAR STORY

Searching for a better way forward

THE RSPB'S DEREK and Sarah Niemann carried out a cotton farm survey in Gujarat, India in 2005. Derek remembers some moving encounters during their trip.

'The Gujarati cotton farmers' children who clustered around us cast shy glances of longing at the binoculars around our necks. They sensed that these long cylinders held remarkable powers by the way we raised them to our eyes, and they understood from our careful handling that these objects must be treated with great respect.

'We soon learned that a way to inspire trust in the farmers was to offer their children the chance to try our binoculars. We placed the straps around their necks as if we were garlanding them with chrysanthemums and they repaid the honour by grasping the binoculars firmly with tiny hands and raising them to their eyes with rapt concentration.

'The little figures rotated on the spot in silent delight, eyes glued to the eye-pieces. We heard gasps of wonder as they saw close-up the rollers, bee-eaters and shrikes that had been their everyday distant companions. And each time, they solemnly offered back our binoculars with both hands, showing the care and reverence for the valued possessions of others that would be beyond even most British children.

'In the port of Mandvi, where men still build wooden ships in the silty harbour, we stopped at a lake where there was an assortment of pelicans, herons and waders. Almost immediately, the inevitable group of boys gathered to investigate. These were well dressed older teenagers and they took the proffered binoculars with courteous, but unsurprised pleasure. Other children sidled up too, but these were much younger and rather tatty, and they kept a cautious, awkward distance, scarcely daring to meet our eyes.

'Our Indian colleague gestured to the little children to come forward. One of the older, well-dressed boys mocked – "they are only rag-pickers' children" and curled his lip in disdain. "They are children," replied our host and beckoned for them to take our binoculars. So it was that scruffy, painfully thin little children stood holding equipment that would have cost their family more than a year's wages.'

Derek and Sarah's survey

The researchers wanted to see if organic cotton production was better for wildlife than other cotton growing methods, and visited the cotton fields of the Kutch region of Gujarat, not far from the border with Pakistan. They teamed up with Dr Shubhalaxmi, an entomologist from the Bombay Natural History Society, to look at invertebrates living amongst the cotton crops. They decided that surveying invertebrates would give them the best chance of finding a difference, if there was one. Unfortunately, the project was limited in time and the team only had access to limited numbers of field types, meaning that the results are inconclusive at this stage. It is hoped that further survey work will make the story clearer.

IMAGE: DEREK NIEMANN

GIVING NEW LIFE TO OLD BINOCULARS

THE UK CONSERVATION charity the RSPB is breathing new life into old binoculars through its imaginative second-hand binocular scheme, which sees optics sent to conservation projects around the world.

Begun in 1985 by the RSPB's international department, the scheme aims to help the thousands of conservation projects overseas that have little or no money and are in dire need of basic optical equipment. Over the last 23 years almost 11,000 binoculars and telescopes have been given to projects from Vietnam to Greece, and from India to Ecuador.

Some time before recycling became popular, the scheme recognised that as people upgrade their optics, old equipment is often put in the back of a cupboard and forgotten about. Instead, it can be put to good use in a range of projects in often remote parts of the world, where access to even simple optical equipment is all but impossible.

Following its launch in the 1980s the scheme was an immediate success. It took another leap forward when the charity approached the retailer Dixons who were offering a 'new for old' binocular deal at the time. The company offered the RSPB the old binoculars that customers had traded in, but the charity had no idea that there would be enough to fill a warehouse. Fortunately, the RSPB's repair man was on friendly terms with his local RAF station and the storage problem was solved, but it took him several years to work through all the binoculars!

After being donated, the optics are looked at by volunteers who decide if they need cleaning, adjusting or re-aligning. Donations are made following requests from partners in the BirdLife International network and from other organisations who have learnt about the scheme.

People supporting the scheme have the thrill of knowing that binoculars, which have given them such enjoyment for years, will soon start a new life bringing people closer to nature in other countries. Over the years the scheme has helped a wide range of projects including:

- Equipping Angola's first ever bird hide in a wetland that provides sanctuary for migratory flamingos
- Helping children in Tanzania to get close-up views of birds on environmental education days
- Supporting wardens in Morrocco's Souss-Massa park which is home to the endangered bald ibis.

A recent project saw the donation of nine binoculars and a telescope and tripod to the Ministry of the Environment, Wildlife Conservation and Tourism of Southern Sudan. Here, they were used straight away during the first waterbirds and wetlands course held in Southern Sudan, attended by 15 trainees and staged at the Nimule National Park on the White Nile. Trainees used the binoculars to identify and count birds along the river, including grey-crowned cranes which were recorded in Sudan for the first time during the survey. The binoculars were the first to be owned by the Ministry, in a region which has been ravaged by civil war for the last 22 years.

The donation of the binoculars can also provide the spark for a career in nature conservation. Several professional conservation officials in donor countries had their first encounter with birds thanks to a binocular given to the scheme.

THE RSPB
SECOND-HAND
BINOCULAR SCHEME

Ten binoculars from the author's reference collection were donated to the RSPB's second-hand binocular scheme shortly before this book went to press. Information about the scheme can be obtained by telephone in the UK on 01767 680551, or by emailing binoenquiries@rspb.org.uk.

Other professional uses

Binoculars help people to carry out their jobs in a wide range of other ways. Angus Clarke is a tree warden living on the south coast of England. His job is to ensure that the trees that grow around the city remain healthy, safe and continue to add to the quality of life of the residents. Every day he uses a binocular to inspect the condition of the branches, helping him make important decisions about which ones have to be lopped off on grounds of safety.

'The binoculars allow me to observe nature without disturbing it. Seeing and identifying are the first steps in the formulation of my ideas on ecological ethics.'

ALDO LEOPOLD

Even Father Christmas needs binoculars! This 1922 postcard from the USA shows a novel use of binoculars in the course of a person's work

Hunting is big business in some countries and binoculars form an important part of the toolkit of the hunting tour leader. For those who want to observe rather than shoot wildlife, another kind of holiday that is increasingly becoming common is the nature-themed vacation. Here, leaders with amazing powers of observation point out everything from elephants to eagles to customers who sometimes tip according to the number of new species spotted on a trip.

Birdies and eagles of the non-feathered kind are firmly on the agenda on the professional golf course. Here, the difference between success and failure depends on the accurate measurement of distances, especially when approaching the green. Special binoculars have been developed that allow such range-finding to take place, thanks to the use of laser technology. Also finding favour with hunters, these allow very accurate estimation of distance, combined with a high quality view of subjects.

People interested in architecture are known to carry a compact binocular around cities so they can study the small details of buildings that grab their attention. A much more critical use of binoculars to look at structures built by humans is the regular bridge inspections that are carried out by surveyors whose role is to ensure that the structural integrity of our bridges is maintained.

One only needs to look at the 2007 bridge failure in Minneapolis, USA, to be reminded of the life and death importance of such work.

'We carried binoculars to Europe on our recent trip – as much to study the frescoes of the Sistine Chapel as to see new kinds of birds in the countryside around the city.'
KATIE WHITE

A final category of professional binocular users are those whose aim is to make a permanent record of what they see, on canvass or film. The author once owned a Docter 8x56 binocular which had previously been used by a well-known British artist while he was painting birds in the field. Its large objective lenses ensured that the maximum amount of light got through to the observer's eyes. Those film-makers and photographers whose subjects are the natural world find a host of special uses for binoculars (➤ see box).

LANDMARK BINOCULAR: THE NIKON 8X30 EII

The pinnacle of 8x30 Porro prism design

THE CONFIGURATION 8x30 must be one of the most popular binocular specifications in history, serving the needs of civilian and military users over almost a hundred years. Although German manufacturers dominated the market for much of the 20th century – notably Zeiss and Leitz – the accolade for the most outstanding achievement in 8x30 design to date must go to Nikon, whose Japanese-made EII model represents a high point of optical excellence.

The Nikon 8x30 EII, introduced in 1999 alongside a larger 10x35 model, is one of those rare examples of a binocular that appears to possess built-in floodlights. Its razor sharp images and high contrast result in a view of the world so detailed and intricate that you could be forgiven for thinking you are right next to the subjects being studied. It has the widest field of view of any high-end x8 binocular currently made, allowing the user to scan vast areas of terrain.

The Nikon 8x30 EII is the latest line in a fine range of high performance 8x30 binoculars from this distinguished Japanese company. An 8x30 E

model was available in the 1980s, and before it a wonderful compact version with similarities to the Zeiss West 8x30 emerged from Japan in the 1950s (➤ page 28). The 8x30 EII has an equally impressive cousin in the shape of the 8x32 SE model, which boasts rubber armouring but does not have the impressive wide field of the 8x30 model.

Rumours continue to persist that the Nikon EII is being phased out as the world becomes obsessed with roof prism models. While these have been denied by Nikon staff, the pressure to move towards roof prism production has already caused the European optical powerhouse Zeiss to stop producing almost all their civilian Porro prism binoculars.

> ### TECHNICAL SPECIFICATION
>
> **NIKON 8X30 EII**
> **Field of view: 8.8° (154 m at 1,000 m)**
> **Apparent field: 70°**
> **Exit pupil diameter: 3.8 mm**
> **Weight: 500 g**

MY BINOCULAR STORY

Watching birds, with big 'nocars'*

WHEN IT COMES to 'nocars' size is important to me, as is what I do with them. To me they are but one of the many tools of my trade, tools that nine times out of ten, have to be carried by me, shanks' pony (although many people have likened me rather to a donkey, upon observing the loads that I carry!). Cameras and lenses tend to be bulky and heavy, particularly in the case of bird photography, so the last thing that I need is another pain in the neck – literally. Therefore I use compact binoculars. After one particular incident, which I'll now relate, I also insist that those binoculars are waterproof – they say that one learns from one's mistakes!

With the help of staff from the RSPB nature reserve at Old Hall Marshes in Essex, I'd been erecting a scaffold tower, just offshore, for photographing tree-nesting cormorants. The base of the tower was in water just deep enough to overtop my waders. If I was careless enough in walking to create my own bow wave, or if I placed my foot in an underwater divot, the already dank existence of my little tootsies would deteriorate further. Whilst assembling the scaffolding, I bent down to fix something, forgetting that my bins were still around my neck. A splash and a gurgle later, they were ruined. Tragedy, more or less in the time it took to read that sentence!

Compact is one thing, and waterproofing another. Although I have a (compact, naturally) telescope available to me, it's rare that I have the capacity to carry it outside of a vehicle. That is why it's of further importance to me that any binoculars that I use have a good resolving power.

There are some very poor optics out there in the world of compact binoculars, even waterproof ones – items that after a few days' intensive use, are likely to hasten your visit to the optician. Compacts are restricted in their light-gathering capability by their proportions, but there are coatings and *coatings*, and then again there is glass, and there is *glass*. You tend to get what you pay for, and the view through one pair of 10x25s might literally shed light and clarity on subjects that are glimpsed only dimly and fuzzily through others. To

IMAGE: ANDY HAY (RSPB-IMAGES.COM)

*See page 193

that end I use Nikon High Grade 10x25 compacts. Eight times magnification I find inadequate, but if you have a stable enough perch x10 binoculars of good quality can offer you almost as much detail as a small 'scope will.

Getting a sneak preview

I often use binoculars for observation when doing 'recces', deciding where to place a hide and watching birds to see whether their behaviour and location make it feasible in the first place. I then tend to use them at each stage of moving the hide in, to make sure that the birds accept it. All essentially for the reason that you'd expect – watching from the distance that binoculars allow, I can be sure that I'm not directly influencing the birds' behaviour.

Depending on the species, it can take three or four days to move a hide into position: after each move you walk away and watch from a distance, quietly 'having kittens' until the birds accept the changes to their environment. I have had kittens over nesting lapwings, feeling not unlike an expectant parent myself, whilst awaiting their approval. And I have had further kittens over hen harriers. One day my assistant Ronnie (a volunteer) and I saw a shape in the heather, near the harriers' nest, which distance and haze transmuted

into a crow – too close for comfort, potentially being a sign that our having put the parents up from the nest had allowed a predator to slip in. Fortunately it proved to be an illusion, created by nerves, and an ironic Hebridean mirage. Nonetheless we chose to take it as a warning, and decided to give the harriers breathing space on that day.

When the end object had been achieved, and the hide had been successfully pitched in a spot that would allow me to get

flight shots of the parents (i.e. not right at the nest), another difficulty cropped up. Initially the male would not accept my presence in the hide – until we employed a gambit with a wax jacket and a yard brush. Leaving a fake lens poking out of the hide when I was away clearly wasn't enough, so we had to employ a trick normally reserved for birds that can count. Who knows, maybe this hen harrier had the numerate gene? Ronnie would walk right up to the hide with me, see me safely installed, and then

walk away, carrying the brush, which in turn was wearing the coat that I had worn on our slog up the hill. Praise be, it worked!

On other occasions, on other heathery hillsides, I've been alone, for instance working with ring ouzels (a shy member of the thrush family), between snow showers in May. In such a case, enhanced powers of observation are even more important to me, as I have to await the moment when both parents are away from the nest, and I can dash into the hide.

Las Grullas!

I was recently involved in a film shoot with our film unit, at various locations in France and Spain. Specifically, I was there as a field assistant to the unit's cameraman. Additional responsibilities were to take 'production stills', and to use the same digital SLR camera to shoot time-lapse sequences.

The species that the film hinges around is the common crane, known also as *grue cendrée* (ashy-coloured crane) in France and as *grulla* in Spain. Both those names and its scientific name, *Grus grus*, have an onomatopoeic quality, hinting at the clear, far-carrying nature of its typical bugling call. The shoot that I was concerned with essentially covered the birds' autumn migration through France, over the Pyrenees, and ultimately

IMAGE: ANGEL GARCIA-ROJO (RSPB-IMAGES.COM)

MY BINOCULAR STORY *Continued*

arriving in their wintering grounds in Extremadura, Spain, amidst rice paddies, cork oaks and jamon on the hoof!

Again I was using binoculars as a tool of the job, only this time mine were a second pair of eyes. The view through any camera viewfinder is restrictive – you've got a great big lump of metal and glass between yourself and an unobstructed view of the world. Whilst using a telephoto lens, the experience is even more like peering through a key hole. So my role was often to warn the team of fast-approaching wildlife, whether that be cranes in a distant V-formation, a flock of Alpine choughs wheeling over the shoulder of a hill, or even a wild boar, wrapped in its own small dust cloud like 'Pig Pen' from the Charlie Brown cartoons, heading towards us at a rate of knots.

Finding the cranes to film was often a trick in itself. You would assume that if you waited at the head of a Pyrenean pass, a known crossing point for many migrants, and cranes in particular, at the right time of year, in reasonable weather conditions, you would stand a good chance of seeing them. Given the numbers involved – thirty-odd thousand – you might, in a romantic dream, expect to be able to walk across the valley via their outstretched wings.

Au contraire! The head of the valley was actually five kilometres wide, and a flock of birds each with a wingspan of two metres, can do a remarkable job of disappearing against distant clouds and hill tops. The calls are a clear indicator of their presence, but amongst such peaks they have an almost ventriloquial quality, reverberating from the crags. As a result, a great deal of time was spent scanning misty horizons through binoculars, both by ourselves, and by other conservationists who were based on the other side of the valley. We were in regular radio contact with them, and found their help to be invaluable, as they were more experienced watchers of migrating birds than ourselves.

The cameraman also needed to obtain footage of the cranes leaving and arriving at their roost sites, and feeding in nearby fields. This necessitated further scanning of distant horizons – we would often leave with the cranes at first light and follow them into the countryside as they sought food. The problem was that they wouldn't necessarily use the same fields each day. Therefore one of my roles was to help in seeking out the choice spots, searching the cold grey horizons

of Champagne, the often colder high plains of Gallocanta, or the comparatively balmy rice paddies of Extremadura.

On other occasions I might be sent out to observe the

movements and timings of the birds at their roosts in a simple division of manpower, whilst others in the team gathered acorns to bait pigs with. The pigs are as elemental to the story as the cranes themselves, the landscape being shaped by and for them. Jamon from the Spanish plains is big business – commanding at the time, 40 Euros a kilo. And therein lies another story – of cork oak savanna being grubbed up in favour of get-rich-quick subsidised rice.

Andy Hay, professional photographer for the RSPB

IMAGE: ANDY HAY (RSPB-IMAGES.COM)

4 Looking up at the skies

Every serious astronomy fan possesses at least one binocular. One of the really exciting things about hobby astronomy is the ability of amateurs to make observations that get the professionals leaping up and down. This chapter brings to life binocular astronomy, outlining the special tools and considerations when looking out into space, and describing some of the vivid personalities in the world of star-gazing. It also tells the story of how astronomy enthusiasts have peered through their giant binoculars and secured their place in history. There is no doubt that binoculars can enable people to enter another world and this chapter explains how astronomers have benefited from them over the ages.

Astronomy is a hobby enjoyed by millions of people across the world

'One of my most influential science teachers at school once told me to go outside on a crisp winter's night and enjoy the view of the night sky with a good pair of binoculars. I'm glad he did, for it opened my eyes to the wonders of the heavens and began a lifelong love of astronomy.'

EMILY NEEDHAM

BINOCULARS HAVE MADE a very important contribution to the academic study of astronomy. They also help to bring the wonder of the heavens within reach of people across the world. Astronomy is one of the few scientific disciplines where amateurs are able to work alongside professionals in order to make important new discoveries. The detection of comets presents the most obvious example, with many groundbreaking observations coming first from people gazing up from their back gardens.

Prior to 1850 most binocular astronomy was carried out by scientists using large and expensive instruments. The publication in the USA in 1888 of Garrett Serviss's landmark volume *Astronomy with an Opera Glass*, however, opened many people's eyes on this side of the Atlantic to the possibilities of astronomy as a hobby. The widespread ownership by the more wealthy classes of opera glasses at this time ensured that, despite their obvious limitations, these instruments could be put to use outside the auditorium, on stars of a different kind. Garrett, a journalist with a passion for the night sky, is regarded as binocular astronomy's first great advocate.

By the time of the appearance of the prismatic binocular in the last decade of the 19th century – and the high power, wide-angle viewing it made possible – astronomy was already a well-established pastime in a number of countries. There were even prominent astronomical societies in both Australia and the UK.

'Thousands of words have been written about the wonders of binocular astronomy. It is wonderful – and in fact it's splendid! Yet it's also grossly underappreciated. If you haven't gotten serious about binocular astronomy, you've been missing out on one of observing's most rewarding pursuits. Pull up a good chair and start drinking in beautiful night sky sights with both eyes.' ALAN ALDER

The science fiction B-movies of the 1940s and 1950s, obsessed as they were with space, other worlds and the threat of alien life, no doubt did much to fuel the public imagination for that which lies beyond our solar system. There are surely many astronomy enthusiasts active today who first gazed up at the night sky as little children, having been inspired by what they saw on the silver screen. The eventual conquering of space later in the 20th century would see eyes aloft across the globe in search of satellites and manned spacecraft that had escaped the grip of earth's gravity.

The availability of bargain price binoculars in recent decades – principally models made in China – has brought binocular astronomy within the reach of many new star gazers. This has helped to nurture the growing amateur interest in astronomy for which the space race of the 1960s was the catalyst.

Instruments of choice
Viewing with two eyes has been shown to be considerably more effective at seeing detail than using just one, so binoculars have been the instruments of choice of astronomy enthusiasts for many centuries.

Astronomy is the quest to see extremely distant and often faint objects more clearly. For this reason the prime consideration for those purchasing binoculars for viewing the night sky is large objective size, since this increases the amount of light reaching the observer's eyes. And it can make the difference between actually seeing some celestial phenomena and being completely ignorant of their presence in your binocular view.

'Such is the ubiquity of binoculars, and so popular is their use both in casual and serious stargazing, that it is quite possible they will outnumber every other class of telescope scanning the night sky at any given time. And that is something to reflect on – or, if you prefer, to refract on.' FRED WATSON

The traditional view maintains that the best binocular for general astronomy is the 7x50 configuration, since it combines impressive light gathering power with the steady image that comes from a magnification of seven. It has been proven that more than 500 features of the moon can identified simply using x7 binoculars alone. This has resulted in a plethora of 7x50 models aimed at the astronomy market. Yet some recent research, published in the well known US astronomy magazine *Sky & Telescope*, showed that observers can actually see more objects with a higher power glass – making x10 or even x15 models ideal for general use, providing they can be held steady. Many users also choose to invest in larger models, with configurations such as 20x80 or 25x100, which require tripods and other stabilisation aids. Those who acquire binoculars solely for astronomical use often choose those with individual focussing eyepieces. These models are easier to waterproof and tend to be more robust in their construction than centre focus versions.

Large objective diameter is the hallmark of most astronomical binoculars. Here, a 20x88 instrument is depicted, a binocular capable of picking out many 'deep sky' objects

The quality of the optical coatings plays an important role in the brightness of binoculars for astronomy. There are typically up to 12 air-to-glass surfaces in both barrels of a binocular, with a small amount of light being lost at each interface. The best binoculars make use of multi-layer coatings that increase the throughput of light to the user's eyes, making even dim objects visible. High quality optical coatings can also improve the contrast of the picture.

Binoculars with a wide field of view are especially suited to astronomy, even more so if image sharpness is maintained close to the edge of the picture. This is more critical than in other observing situations as stars that might otherwise be visible can become grossly deformed at the edge of the field of view in models

LANDMARK BINOCULAR: THE CANON 10X30 IMAGE STABILISED

Steady views of the heavens

ALTHOUGH FUJINON AND Nikon were the first companies to make civilian binoculars with in-built stabilisation devices, it was Canon that managed to achieve the breakthrough of producing light, compact models at a price point to tempt the masses. Their best-selling range of image stabilisation binoculars is crowned by what is widely considered to the pick of the bunch in terms of value for money – the 10x30IS.

The Canon 10x30IS, in common with the other models in the range, uses the 'vary angle' stabilisation method. The binocular incorporates battery-powered microprocessors that control the prisms, sensing horizontal and vertical changes in angle and making tiny adjustments to bring rock-steady viewing. The result, when the stabilisation button is depressed, is visually stunning and allows the observer to see detail that would otherwise only be seen with a tripod-mounted binocular. Canon also incorporated field-flattering elements in these binoculars to give impressive edge-to-edge sharpness to the image, adding considerably to the quality of the optics.

The appeal of the Canon 10x30IS is not just down to its impressive image stabilising mechanism. However, it has at its heart a very fine optical system and state-of-the-art 'super spectra' optical coatings

which render amazingly bright images, defying the 30 mm objective diameter. Close inspection of the binocular body reveals that this Porro prism model is made in Japan – the home of the finest binoculars of this specification. So much binocular production has been transferred to China in recent years that it is now rare to find models stamped 'made in Japan'. For a x10 binocular the Canon 10x30IS is also fairly small and compact, and sits very comfortably in the hand, adding to its appeal to wide range of users.

The Canon 10x30IS has become popular with astronomy enthusiasts despite its small objective lenses, as well as being snapped up by boat owners, birdwatchers and a host of other users. There are parallel models from Canon from x8 up to x18 magnification, some of which are waterproof. At the time of writing there is no high quality competitor for the smaller image stabilised models from Canon such as the 10x30IS, and for some online retailers this innovative model is one of the best-selling of all their binoculars.

TECHNICAL SPECIFICATION

Canon 10x30IS
Field of view: 6.0° (105 m at 1,000 m)
Apparent field: 60°
Exit pupil diameter: 3 mm
Weight: 600 g

with poor peripheral sharpness. This has made those binoculars with 'field flattening' lens elements especially popular with astronomers – such as the various models by Fujinon.

The presence of false colour around subjects such as stars and planets can interfere with the enjoyment of binocular astronomy. This is caused by the optical characteristics of the prisms and lenses used in binoculars, but varies from model to model. Users report that the more you pay, the less false colour is a problem and in lower power instruments (i.e. those with a magnification of x10 or less) the phenomenon is less noticeable than in binoculars of higher power.

'The moon provides an attractive binocular object even for those people who do not call themselves astronomers. For those whose eyes have drunk from the lunar surface, few can surely forget the first time they saw a string of craters in half-shadow at the sunlit edge of our own little satellite.' JENNY BRYANT

Some extremely large high power binoculars have been made. King among these is the leviathan Fujinon 25x150, the world's heaviest prismatic binocular, which at 18.5 kg is impossible to hand hold. The huge price of this formidable instrument does not deter buyers from also investing in some remarkable devices to hold the Fujinon steady. The most extraordinary of these is a 'Starchair' in which the observer sits, with the binoculars suspended overhead. A different take on 'huge objective' astronomy comes in the form of the recent appearance of binocular telescopes incorporating mirror systems. These instruments, known as reverse binoculars, require unconventional viewing, with the observer tilting his or her head towards the ground to access the eyepieces. Astronomers sometimes use 'binoviewers' to make two-eyed observations through their telescopes. Although these are not really binoculars, since the devices split the light from one telescope into the two light paths of the binoviewer lenses, they give the comfort and added resolution of binocular viewing.

Observing tactics

Many enthusiasts describe the principal joy of binocular astronomy to be the ease with which one can go outside and start observing straight away, without being encumbered with other paraphernalia. It also helps that an impressive view of the night sky can be obtained by using a binocular that costs less than £100, compared to the high price of state-of-the-art telescopes. Many astronomical subjects can be seen very well in binoculars, and for some faint and diffuse objects in the catalogue, such as nebulae, they may even represent the best instruments for study.

Clear skies and steady viewing are the holy grail of astronomers. The reason that low power binoculars are often popular with astronomers is that they can be easily hand-held and carried around the neck of the observer. Experienced

www.starchair.com

binocular sky watchers maintain that viewing from a chair is far steadier and more comfortable than when standing up, and a range of suitable observing chairs has been improvised for astronomy.

Much effort is placed at stabilising larger aperture binoculars using a variety of tripod-like stands and other devices. Many of these are home made and astronomy magazines often contain instructions and reviews of different models. This obsession with steadiness has resulted in the binocular models with in-built stabilisation becoming the chosen instrument of many astronomers – amateur and professional alike. Internet forums buzz with the latest reviews, product launches and news, with the models from Canon currently being the most sought after.

Huge binoculars need huge mounts. This futuristic 'star chair' device allows the user complete control of their giant binoculars

'For any binoculars to give their best, they need to be held steady. It's amazing how little jiggling it takes to seriously impair the view!' ALAN ALDER

When observing the night sky through binoculars astronomy enthusiasts use the 'averted gaze' technique. By concentrating on the edge of the field while still keeping objects near the centre, they take advantage of the eye's ability to pick up fainter objects at its periphery. This phenomenon is due to the higher concentration of the more light-sensitive rod cells at the edge of the eye. Observers of variable stars still use the uniform illumination of binoculars to make observations of the brightness of their subjects, relative to surrounding stars in the field of view.

Astronomy enthusiasts organise 'star parties' where the heavens can be viewed through a wide range of optical instruments. Binocular observation and testing can form an important part of such gatherings and it is not unusual to find

The latest innovation in binocular astronomy sees the introduction of huge mirror systems to bring spectacular views of the night sky to the observer. The high price of these ultimate instruments has led to the catch phrase 'Think of it as a cross between a Harley and a telescope!'

binoculars worth collectively many tens of thousands of pounds on display. They are used in conjunction with much more powerful telescopes to allow access to the widest range of objects in the night sky.

> *'Above all, my biggest boost comes from young children who look forward to the star party each year. I cherish their smiles because they tell me we're doing something right: we're reaching the younger generations and are teaching them about the beauty of the heavens.'* ORGANSIER OF THE TAINAI STAR PARTY IN JAPAN

This US-made product allows compact binocular to be fixed to a tripod, walking pole or window clamp – indeed any device that incorporates a tripod bush

Outside the military arena, astronomy is one of the few civilian applications of binoculars to take advantage of filters. Some models incorporate special filters that reduce the characteristic yellow light of sodium-discharge street lamps, making viewing in light-polluted skies easier. Other binoculars, usually those with high price tags, can be fitted with 'nebula filters' which increase contrast when observing these faint objects. A further sample are equipped with so-called solar filters that permit safe observation of the sun by cutting out over 99% of the incoming light. A few people have been tragically blinded by looking at the sun with their conventional binoculars, unaware of the damage it can cause.

MY BINOCULAR STORY

Thanks Uncle Tony

A HIGHLIGHT OF my childhood years was the periodic astronomy sessions that I enjoyed with my Uncle Tony. Although we successfully made observations in the polluted skies above my home in Manchester, it was the crystal clear evenings of rural south Wales that provided some of the most memorable sightings.

Uncle Tony helped me to set up my first telescope, but he also taught me a lot about binocular astronomy too. As a young boy I was lulled into thinking that high power optics must be best for observing the night sky, when Uncle Tony knew best. His technical knowledge and enthusiasm for the topic fired up my own interest in astronomy and optical instruments.

I will always be especially grateful to my Uncle Tony for opening up my world to the delights of satellite observation. I remember one particular evening when he showed me how to use the satellite predictions in a national newspaper. We studied what was printed, then positioned ourselves outdoors with a compass on hand to ensure we were facing in the correct direction. With a red-filter torch to the ready to help keep our eyes adapted to the dark sky, we kept track of the time while concentrating closely on the segment of the night sky where we expected the satellites to appear.

I will never forget the first time I saw one of these star-like objects which orbit the earth at great speed. Sure enough, right on cue, there it was careering across the night sky at tens of thousands of miles an hour. The look on my face when I headed indoors to tell my parents what I had seen must have told all.

I continue to be fascinated by the night time observation of satellites which seem to pass most people by. Only last year a friend was thrilled as I pointed out the International Space Station on a cold winter's night as we left work. Uncle Tony would have been proud of me!

BB

Watching the sunset

On first glance this observer appears to be ignoring the vital rule that you must not look directly at the sun with binoculars unless using special filters. It soon becomes apparent, however, that something entirely different is lighting up his world

A device favoured by some astronomy buffs is a special Sky Window which observers place on the ground so they can get a more comfortable view of the night sky above their heads. By mounting their binocular in the frame, a natural head position can be maintained while still viewing the sky above.

Those astronomy buffs who enjoy using binoculars have some helpful publications to guide their nocturnal sojourns. They include several volumes on observing the moon, as well as several more general books on binocular astronomy. These are among the only publications that deal with the use of binoculars for a specific pastime. A recent brace of titles (Tonkin 2006; Scagell & Frydman 2007) also include miniature reviews of some of the most popular binoculars for astronomy.

Many magazines for astronomers are also published in countries where the hobby is popular. The British publication *Sky at Night* issues a monthly pullout stargazing guide which includes a section devoted to binocular objects, and other well-established astronomy magazines in the USA and Europe have helped to publicise the benefits of binocular astronomy. They have also featured observing advice and frequently include comparative reviews of binoculars from different makers. Naturally, such magazines have also been the place for companies to place some of their most high profile advertisements. Important astronomical events have also provided binocular marketeers with additional opportunities to extol the celestial virtues of binoculars – most notably the much-heralded re-appearance of Halley's comet in 1986.

Tasco provided a special free 'Comet-Finder Kit' to accompany binocular purchases in the run up to the reappearance of Halley's comet in 1986

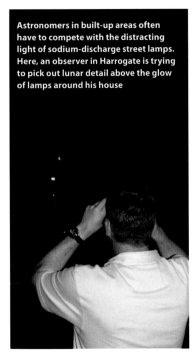

Astronomers in built-up areas often have to compete with the distracting light of sodium-discharge street lamps. Here, an observer in Harrogate is trying to pick out lunar detail above the glow of lamps around his house

SIR PATRICK'S BINOCULARS

Writing in his book, *Exploring the Night Sky with Binoculars* (2000), Sir Patrick Moore explains that seven different binoculars form part of his toolkit for observing from his base in the dark skies of rural Sussex. They are listed below, together with some remarks from Sir Patrick.

3x20 opera glass	'Unless you can find a pair cheaply, I would advise against them'
7x50	'An excellent choice for general viewing'
8.5x50	'The light grasp is adequate for this magnification and the binoculars can still be hand-held'
8x50	'Excellent'
11x80	'Very fine with a reasonable field of view and a good light-grasp, though they are rather too heavy to be properly handheld'
12x40	'The smaller aperture and higher magnification means that the images are not so bright as in former pairs, and the field of view smaller still'
20x70	'When they have been properly set up, they give splendid results...the moon shows a wealth of detail'

In his book, *Exploring the Night Sky with Binoculars*, which actually set the mould for titles on binocular astronomy, celebrated British astronomer Sir Patrick Moore describes the varied instruments in his personal collection. As well as being the presenter of the world's longest running TV programme with the same host (BBC TV's *The Sky at Night*), Sir Patrick has made some important contributions to the field of astronomy through observations carried out from his back garden observatory in Sussex.

Sir Patrick is not alone in possessing a wide range of binoculars to make the most of his passion. The US-based internet forum *Cloudy Nights* allows members to share their views on a whole host of hot topics in astronomy, with postings on equipment being a particular favourite. It is not unusual to see members, who often sign off with a list of their astronomy equipment, mention over five different binocular models – all with specific uses.

The popularity of astronomy as a hobby has led to the establishment of a special sector of the tourism industry aimed at this market. While some companies offer exotic trips to see the next solar eclipse through specially-adapted binoculars, others tempt enthusiasts with the promise of dark skies and a range of high quality equipment. Astronomy also provides an unconventional use for binoculars during partial and full solar eclipses. During such exciting periods, people are encouraged by national astronomy bodies to protect their eyes by projecting the image of the sun onto a flat surface.

The popularity of binocular astronomy extends beyond amateurs, as such instruments are a useful tool for professionals too. There are reports of professional

Astronomy tourists can take their binoculars to special locations where dark skies are guaranteed, such as this fine observing base set amid the dramatic landscape of southwest Scotland

astronomers relieving the stress of observing through large telescopes by spending a few minutes outside, looking at the crisp night sky above their observatories with a hand-held binocular. Binoculars are now considered such an essential part of any astronomer's toolkit that they feature as one of only six pewter tokens in the astronomy version of the poular board game monopoly, taking pride of place alongside the Hubble Space Telescope no less!

The quest for comets and novae

For many astronomy fans – not just those observing in the clear skies above Japan such as the late Yuji Hyakutake – a highlight of the hobby is the prospect of finding a comet that will ultimately bear their name. In the UK George Alcock used a mounted war-time 25x105 binocular telescope to make a string

of important observations, discovering no less than four comets between 1959 and 1983. He even discovered one comet with his handheld 15x80 binoculars through a double-glazed window! Alcock is also known for finding some important novae – brilliant thermonuclear blasts that happen on the surface of distant stars. These are notoriously difficult objects to observe.

In another part of Europe, Portuguese nova hunter extraordinaire Alfredo Pereira uses some special techniques to maximise his chances of making a discovery. Following in the footsteps of great nova hunters before him, Pereira does not use traditional star charts but instead creates his own miniature constellations out of the stars he sees through binoculars. After memorising the patterns he sees, he is able to pick out the tell-tale signs of a new nova. The fact that he spends one and a half hours observing each clear night – regardless of the moon's phase – means that Pereira is well placed to make new observations.

George Alcock, comet-hunter extraordinaire, seen here with his World War II 25x105 binocular, manufactured by the German firm Schneider

IMAGE: BAA ARCHIVES

'I caught a nova just a few minutes after I had started another evening session. I had swept Scutum and raising the 14x100s northeast I scanned central Aquila where I go deep into magnitude 8.5. I had the intention of switching to 9x34s since these areas were higher in the sky, but then I saw a bright object that completely disturbed even the main "skeleton" of my binocular patterns…My heart pounded.'

ALFREDO PEREIRA, ON FINDING HIS FIRST NOVA IN

1999 THROUGH AN OPEN WINDOW IN HIS HOUSE

The appearance in 1991 and 1996 of large two telescopes with automatic comet discovery features was thought to have heralded a new era when amateur comet hunters' dreams of ever finding a new object were shattered. However, since 2000 there has been a string of new comet discoveries by amateurs, despite the technological power of the massive new telescopes. Between 2000 and 2004 three of the twelve new comets sighted were found simply by observers using binoculars.

Comet and nova hunters are very dedicated individuals. When Japanese astronomer Kaoru Ikeya co-discovered a comet in 2002 he had been sweeping the night sky for 35 years, without a single find! And New Zealander Albert Jones had to wait 54 years from the discovery of his first comet in 1946 to his last in 2000. Fortune as well as fame may await the lucky few: since 1998 over $20,000 has been distributed annually among amateur comet discoverers from the Edgar Wilson Award.

> *'Historically, many Japanese patrollers have favoured the superb Fujinon 25x150 binoculars and these instruments are something of a status symbol amongst Japanese observers.'*
>
> MARTIN MOBBERLEY

The size of a house

A unique astronomical instrument is housed in its own special building in the mountains above Safford, Arizona, USA. This is the home of the Large Binocular Telescope, the largest 'binocular' ever built, which is the crowing glory of the Mt Graham International Observatory. The instrument uses two giant 8.4 metre mirrors mounted side by side, and is so complex that it took a decade to build.

The idea behind the LBT, as it is known, is to combine the images of the two individual telescopes to simulate the light gathering power of a larger instrument. In this sense it is not strictly a binocular and is certainly not one that can be viewed through both eyes of an observer. Rather, it uses some of the principles of binocular design to increase image quality when viewing the night sky, while still making the instrument easier to work with than a giant single mirror telescope. The twin mirror design increases resolving power compared to a conventional instrument, a property that binocular users benefit from on a much smaller scale when viewing through the two barrels of their prismatic binoculars.

In 2008 the LBT was the world's highest resolution and most technologically advanced telescope, creating images in the infrared with ten times the resolution of the Hubble Space Telescope. The designers hope that the LBT will help to discover and observe planets around distant stars. It will also play a role in observing planet forming regions in our own Milky Way, with the hope of making new and exciting discoveries.

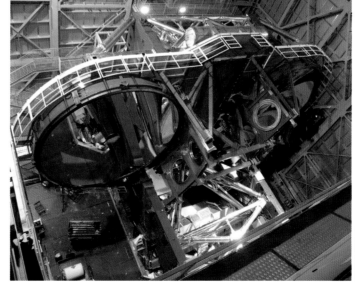

IMAGE: R. BERTRAM

5 The natural world

Binoculars provide life-changing moments when we get close to the natural world, and most people owning a binocular have at least one special story of their own to tell. Perhaps more than any other pastime, binoculars have enhanced nature observation; they have allowed people to witness up close the often secret world of animals. As we shall see in this chapter they may have even helped to turn the tide away from bird collecting and hunting in favour of conservation. But the world of binoculars and natural history also has its own share of fashions, trends and fads. It also has some larger than life characters who have lent their names to some of the prominent names in optics.

Observing the natural world is a joy enjoyed by people of all ages

'It was a still dawn and the sun was just lifting over the forest-cloaked hillside as whiffs of cloud hovered in the canopy. Below me birds came to drink at one of the few pools left in an old stream bed. I was secluded in a remote corner of Ecuador, looking for the beautiful and endangered ochre-bellied dove. It is one of 50 species of bird that makes its home in the dry forests that cling to the last undisturbed parts of this stunning Andean country and its neighbour Peru, but is found no-where else on earth. I had studied lifeless specimens of this bird at the natural history museum, but nothing could prepare me for the moment when I lifted my binoculars and its rich plumage greeted my eyes for the first time. I was consumed by a buffet of beetroot purple, salmon and tangerine and I knew that, for a few wonderful moments, I was the only man on earth whose eyes were fixed on this mysterious species.'

JARVIS HAYES, *TRAVELS IN TUMBESIA*

IT HAS BEEN said that high quality prismatic binoculars transformed the study of birds from a pastime that required a gun to one that simply needed good optical glass. Certainly during much of the 1800s low power, narrow angle Galilean binoculars made close observation of birds difficult. It is perhaps not surprising that this was the heyday of bird collecting, especially in Europe and North America. This was fuelled partly by the large museums wishing to expand their natural history collections, but also by the desires of wealthy private individuals, for whom cases of stuffed birds were often seen as a status symbol.

Yet even before prismatic binoculars were pioneered it appears that bird lovers sporting Galilean binoculars managed to make quite a fuss among the bird hunting fraternity – in one part of the world at least. Writing about this phenomenon in his book, *Of a feather: a brief history of American birding* (2007), Scott Wiedensaul tells us that these early conservationists were known as 'opera glass fiends' by hunters. One frustrated hunter is reported to have said, 'But the opera glass fiends! They live too near the great heart of nature to know anything of her head or hands, or do a stroke of sensible work, even to protect birds.'

'The eyes of man function at comparatively close ranges. Unaided, they limit his enjoyment of outdoor life to his immediate surroundings and restrict his usefulness in many operations. But through optics he has gained other and far-seeing eyes to help his own. Binoculars are made to lift his horizon and broaden his landscape, to unveil Nature's inaccessible reaches, to expose hidden dangers of the deep.' BAUSCH & LOMB BINOCULAR ADVERTISEMENT (1920)

Despite such reports, it is difficult to over-estimate the impact that Zeiss's first prismatic binoculars (introduced in 1894) must have had on natural historians. Now for the first time it was possible to enjoy high quality three dimensional images of distant subjects, with the added benefit of a much wider angle of view than previously possible. This allowed observers to detect movement at the periphery of the field that would simply not have been visible in Galilean glasses. Zeiss fully recognised the significance of their innovative product, and their patent protected the company for 15 years from copycat products from their rivals (➤ page 19).

The impressive resolution of these early Zeiss binoculars often comes as a surprise to modern observers. In the first few years of the company's binocular production, prisms and lenses were made by hand and were very highly polished, producing outstanding image quality. The author has owned an early 8x20 Jena-made glass dating from about 1900 that out-resolves almost every modern x8 binocular, much to the amazement of those who look through it today.

So by the beginning of the 20th century manufacturers such as Zeiss were already producing binoculars that compare favourably with modern day instruments, but their high price meant that they were only likely to be owned by the well-to-do of the day. That situation had scarcely changed fifty years later, when the Zeiss West 8x30 of the 1950s cost the equivalent of six weeks' wages for a professional in the UK. Even the products of less prestigious manufacturers seemed out of reach for most people. It was only a decade or so after the end of World War II, when Japan became a major force in binocular production, that prices of most civilian models began to fall to within the compass of most working people – and even then they remained something of a treasured item.

Feather detail

This price accessibility of binoculars following World War II, coupled with the increased leisure time that security and rising prosperity brought, meant that nature observation – and birdwatching in particular – became a much more popular pastime. This coincided with the publication in the 1950s on both sides of the Atlantic of comprehensive field guides to birds that for the first time enabled laypeople to be able to put a name to most bird species – providing they were equipped with a decent binocular.

During the immediate post-war years surplus military optics became available in those countries which finally disentangled themselves from international conflicts. For a time this led to many birdwatchers in the UK using rather heavy, cumbersome models with individual eyepiece focussing, which nevertheless rendered impressive views. Some of these had their lenses coated before being released to the public to improve their light transmission. Photographs from the UK from this period often show birdwatchers sporting binoculars of the Porro II configuration (◆ page 13), which were originally made in large numbers for military purposes by firms such as Ross and Barr & Stroud.

Increased leisure time on both sides of the Atlantic in the post war years meant that people were tempted to explore the great outdoors in increasing numbers

> *'There is only one moderately expensive tool which need stand in the way of anyone's evolution from a keen birdwatcher to a first-class ornithologist – this is, a good pair of field glasses.'*
>
> JAMES FISHER

Although early binocular entrepreneurs such as David Bushnell talked to birdwatchers about their specific binocular needs in the 1950s, it seems that Swift was the first company to see the potential for a binocular designed *specifically* for birdwatchers. In producing its 8.5x44 model, which was eventually endorsed by the US National Audubon Society (the country's largest bird conservation charity), it succeeded in designing a landmark binocular which launched in 1961 and is still in existence (◆ see box). Spurred on by the success of Swift, other companies followed suit, with the appearance in the 1980s of an Audubon-endorsed Bausch & Lomb range (7x26, 8x36 and 10x40; no longer made) and more recently a

MY BINOCULAR STORY

The big sit

ON A SPRING day on the North Norfolk coast, a man and a woman are perched on a raised piece of land at the bottom of their garden, overlooking the marshes. Holiday makers passing by on the coast road below could be forgiven for thinking that this binocular-clad couple are simply taking a pleasant cup of tea while they scan the marshes from their vantage-point. Little do they know, however, that a 'big sit' is taking place, the observers in question have been in position since before dawn and will still be there seventeen hours later after the sun has gone down!

Steve and Liz Harris are among a growing band of enthusiasts for surely the most eco-friendly kind of birdwatching experience: counting the number of species seen or heard from a single viewpoint during the course of just one day. The big sit phenomenon, which first started in the 1980s in the USA, challenges observers to first find a vantage-point from where a wide range of habitats can be viewed. The Harris's have a distinct advantage in this respect, since their home in the Norfolk village of Salthouse commands a wonderful 180 degree panorama over the coast, taking in scrub, woodlands, marshes, grassland and even views over the North Sea.

Their day begins well before dawn, in order to catch nocturnal species such as nightjars and owls that hunt in the area before the sun rises. Steve and Liz position themselves on 'the hump', an area of built-up ground at the far end of the garden that gives them the most uninterrupted views of the area. A wide range of optical equipment is used, including hand-held x8 and tripod-mounted x15 binoculars, plus a pair of telescopes. The tripod mounting of binoculars helps Steve and Liz to scan wide areas of terrain in considerable comfort, with one of the pair using a formidable Zeiss West 15x60 GAT binocular and the other an equally superb Docter Nobilem 15x60.

Various observation strategies are used to maximise the number of species being recorded. Special attention is paid to 'hotspots' – areas where birds tend to congregate, and both observers are aware that lighting conditions make viewing to the west easier in the morning and to the east better in the evening. Close attention is paid to the sea in the hours after dawn, allowing important observations to be made before the heat-haze begins to make viewing difficult.

Liz admits that although a

brace of roof prism models named the Audubon Equinox (8x42 and 10x42). The Audubon society is said to take great interest in only endorsing binoculars of fine optical quality, hence all the above mentioned models represent excellent value for money.

> *'Perhaps by no one else is a good pair of binoculars so appreciated as by the enthusiastic birdwatcher – a pair that is light, focuses rapidly and closely with center wheel, and has a sharp, bright image to define the minutest detail of feathering and subtlest of colour shading.'*
> HENRY PAUL

On the other side of the Atlantic in 1996 the Royal Society for the Protection of Birds (RSPB) put its name to a range of binoculars chosen and marketed in the UK in collaboration with the optics company Viking. Though slow to realise the potential of its brand as a force for selling optics, RSPB

big sit sounds a little eccentric it can soon become very addictive. Close observation of this sort enables you to learn so much about the birds of a specific area and provides real insights into the behaviour of some species. Naturally, detailed observation of this sort brings its rewards in terms of special sightings too. Over the years the Harris's have sighted ospreys, cranes and spoonbills – all species which would be the highlight of a day's birdwatching in most parts of England. There

have also been some bizarre observations, such as the time Steve watched a male Mandarin duck make its way along the dyke below the house.

The coastal location for their big sit guarantees Steve and Liz an insight into migration patterns. They plan their big sits for spring and autumn, both periods when many bird species are on the move, and there is always a thrill when small migrants such as wheatears and whinchat start to move through. Migration brings

unexpected sightings too, such as the time the couple watched a short-eared owl gain height over the shingle-bank before heading out over the ocean towards its Scandinavian breeding grounds.

Steve and Liz Harris always look forward to their big sits and plan to continue doing them for many years to come. The days can be tiring and at times frustrating, but they can also be exhilarating, exciting and – as passing visitors might like to think – even relaxing. Enjoying optics is an important part of the day, and Steve and Liz know that they would not be able to identify over 90 species in a single day were it not for the binoculars that accompany them to the mound on these landmark days.

ABOVE: The graceful avocet, one of the wading birds that Steve and Liz Harris enjoy watching during their 'big sits'

optics now generates significant sales for the charity, which is the largest conservation organisation in Europe. The fact that it has over one million members, many new to birdwatching, means it has something of a captive audience for its good value optical equipment.

The use of binoculars is now surely associated with birdwatchers more than any other user group. You cannot really call yourself a birdwatcher if you do not own a binocular. Yet newcomers to birdwatching are often unaware that a whole raft of unwritten rules govern the use of binoculars for their chosen hobby – rules that if broken can result in frowns of disapproval from fellow birders (➧ page 89). While such rules are less stringently applied than a few decades ago – birdwatching is thankfully a much more inclusive hobby than it used to be – they still form a fascinating part of the social history of binoculars. Incidentally, these rules also extend to the clothing birdwatchers wear and their behaviour when out in the field.

LANDMARK BINOCULAR: THE SWIFT AUDUBON 8.5X44

The first birdwatching binocular

WHILE THE TOP European makers were focussing their attention on the manufacturing and marketing of sleek new roof prism binoculars, one of the finest Porro prism models ever to be made emerged from a US-Japanese collaboration. The Audubon 8.5x44, from the well-known American company Swift, also can legitimately claim to be the first binocular designed specifically for birdwatching.

Swift had been in existence since 1926, producing a variety of optical instruments for domestic and overseas customers. In the early 1960s the company took a radical step forward in its binocular design – it seems that the Swift Audubon 8.5x44 was conceived as a birding binocular right from the outset. The project team even used the results of a 1950s survey of ornithologists' needs to help perfect the design of the binocular.

The first Swift Audubon (model 804 as it was known) was designed by Mr Tamura of the Tamron Optical Company, Japan, whose company would also make the instrument for a decade after its launch in 1961. Its key design features were to set the mould for this formidable binocular in years to come. They included the use of a five element Erfle eyepiece which gave very wide-field views, prisms made of high quality barium crown glass and special optical coatings.

Swift apparently patented the Audubon name in the early 1960s, which was most likely done in conjunction with marketing the first version of the binocular. It seems that only some years later did discussions began with the National Audubon Society of the USA that would see the Swift Audubon become the first binocular to gain the society's official endorsement.

The organisation is also reported to have had specialist input into the revised Audubon model that appeared in 1995.

For some reason, Swift were slow to recognise the marketing advantage of its association with this prestigious American environmental organisation, and indeed the National Audubon Society's logo was never stamped on the binocular itself. Although the licensing agreement with the society was to end, as was Swift's control of the Audubon product name which passed into the public domain, the name continued to live on in a range of binoculars made by Swift.

There have been four main incarnations of the Swift Audubon 8.5x44: two chunky versions which were at the top of price-conscious birders' wish lists for much of the 1960s and 1970s; a slimmer and lighter model that emerged in the mid-1980s; and the latest rubber armoured and waterproof model, launched in 2005, and given the new product code 820. The last two versions of this classic binocular have been available with special low dispersion ED glass, which reduces chromatic aberration and improves viewing still further.

The Swift Audubon 8.5x44 is one of the rare examples of a binocular that has only ever had rave reviews. Magazine and websites are replete with compliments for this now iconic binocular. In the best examples, its centre resolution matches that of any binocular at any price and it has been compared favourably with such high-end company as the Swarovski 8.5x42 EL. All the models have provided very comfortable wide-angle views, with the earliest version having the widest apparent field of 72 degrees.

Curiously, most people agree that the optical performance of the latest model does not improve on the previous two. In fact independent tests have shown that the 820 does not resolve detail as well as the 804 HR5 launched in 1989, though it does produce more colour-faithful images, avoiding the bluish hues of previous models.

Although other Swift binoculars bore the name 'Audubon' (notably a 10x50 wide-angle model), it was the 8.5x44 model that proved to be the landmark achievement. The latest model is still very popular with birders today, and collectors remain eager to lay their hands on earlier incarnations of this classic binocular, with the 804 ED version being the most sought after.

TECHNICAL SPECIFICATION

SWIFT AUDUBON 8.5X44 MODEL A
Field of view: 8.5° (149 m at 1,000 m)
Apparent field: 72°
Exit pupil diameter: 5.2 mm
Weight: 1089 g

TECHNICAL SPECIFICATION

SWIFT AUDUBON 8.5X44 MODEL B
Field of view: 8.5° (149 m at 1,000 m)
Apparent field: 72°
Exit pupil diameter: 5.2 mm
Weight: 1089 g

TECHNICAL SPECIFICATION

SWIFT AUDUBON 8.5X44 MODEL C
Field of view: 8.2° (144 m at 1,000 m)
Apparent field: 70°
Exit pupil diameter: 5.2 mm
Weight: 800 g

TECHNICAL SPECIFICATION

SWIFT AUDUBON 8.5X44 MODEL D
Field of view: 8.2° (144 m at 1,000 m)
Apparent field: 70°
Exit pupil diameter: 5.2 mm
Weight: 800 g

BIRDWATCHING WITH BINOCULARS – THE UNWRITTEN RULES

1. Binoculars should not look new as this suggests you might be a 'dude' (someone new the hobby). Some birders in the 1980s were even known the distress the exterior of their binoculars as soon as they bought them to give a weathered effect.

2. The lenses should be immaculately clean – while exterior dirt is approved of as it shows you get out often, dirt on the lenses is a no go area since it reduces the clarity of the image and hence makes identifications more difficult.

3. The strap should be a short as possible – this means that the binocular is easy to bring to your face to look at birds. Waist-length straps that result in a wild swinging motion are completely out.

4. Binoculars should only ever be kept in their cases when at home – to be seen with a binocular in its case while out in the field is a sure sign that you are not taking the hobby seriously. If you spot a bird, it might have gone by the time you've fumbled your binoculars out of their case.

5. Binocular straps should be adorned with metal leg rings of birds – these ideally should be taken from dead birds you have found while out birding. Such rings are used to study the migration patterns of birds and bear a unique number making it possible to determine exactly when and where the bird was first trapped.

IMAGE: RICHARD LOW

Binoculars are used as road-side signs in North Carolina, USA, to alert drivers to nature viewing sites

One of the important general principles for birdwatchers is always to have their binoculars handy, ready to identify the species they encounter. This even extends to when they are *inside* their homes, in their cars, at work or sat at their desks. Thus, many birdwatchers have reasonably-priced spare binoculars to allow them to do this, keeping them in strategically-placed locations so they are always at hand. Internet forums hum with correspondence on such idiosyncratic topics as 'binoculars for the car' or 'desk-top bins'.

Binoculars allow natural history observations to be made that are thrilling and sometimes remarkable. These range from sightings of two charismatic birds of prey in the same binocular view – such as marsh and Montagu's harrier over an English marsh – to the observation of exotic avian rarities from America (parula warbler) and eastern Asia (yellow-browed warbler) sharing the same tree-top in Cornwall, one of the UK's prime localities for rare birds.

It is not unusual to find birdwatchers who are emotionally attached to their binoculars. Binoculars are special to birders because they are the key that unlocks the sometimes secret world of birds. Some of the most memorable experiences in a birder's life may have been made possible through their binoculars, and as such they can become treasured items in their own right. While many birders are eager to upgrade their optics to enjoy even clearer views of the natural world, they may be reluctant to sell their old binoculars due to the memories that they evoke. A few even choose not to upgrade in favour of using rather outdated models, that nonetheless still perform well and bring with them the familiarity of an old friend. The author has even known birders who keep a list of species seen through a particular binocular!

> 'There can be little doubt that the best general magnification of a pair of binoculars is a 7x or an 8x. A magnification of this size is not too great, does not strain or 'pull' the eyes, and when you are shivering in a cold north-easter on the edge of a reservoir or on the shore, your shivering will not be so magnified as to make it impossible to distinguish between an oiled scoter and an oil drum.'
>
> PETER CONDER

Birdwatchers use binoculars in two main ways: they look at birds and they look for them. While the first use is most familiar to the non-birdwatching fraternity it can sometimes come as a surprise that birders sometimes spend more time scanning for birds than actually seeing them. This is why wide-angle binoculars are favoured by birders – it is helpful to see movement at the edges of the field of view even if the subject is not entirely sharp. The author has frequently been asked while out birding what he is looking at, only to give the reply, 'Nothing, but I'm hoping to see something if I look hard enough!'.

MY BINOCULAR STORY

The web of life

I EXPERIENCED A strange phenomenon when using binoculars over the course of a two week caravan holiday with my family in the French Ardèche. On the first morning of the trip I headed out shortly after dawn, eager to see which birds were to be found along the tracks into the Maquis vegetation on the hillsides around the campsite. As the May sunshine warmed my cheeks the day started well, with lovely views of hoopoe, woodchat shrike and repeated views of a male sub-alpine warbler visiting a nest. This was perfect Mediterranean birding.

Then I noticed something strange appear in the right barrel of my binocular. As I turned them up to view the sky, a foreign object could be clearly seen lurking inside the barrel. I was astonished when closer inspection revealed this to be a tiny spider – alive and investigating the inside of my binocular! I couldn't wait to get back to the campsite to show my family what I had found.

Over the course of the holiday we took great pleasure in watching the day to day progress of the spider. Was he is view today? Had he grown in size? Would he complete the exciting journey to the other barrel? So many questions and so much fun all caused by this tiny insect!

Things got very exciting when he began to spin a web on the day that we were due to visit a canyon famed for nesting Alpine swifts, one of Europe's most agile and acrobatic birds and a true master of the skies. The views of the birds were made all the more intriguing when viewed through the binocular, which now had a complete web clearly visible with the right eye. The swifts ducked in and out of view, as if trying to dodge a giant arachnid that had laid its web across the canyon. A true nature spectacle!

On return to the UK I sent the binocular to the manufacturer, with a covering letter that must have made quite amusing reading to the customer service department. How, I wondered, could this apparently sealed binocular let in a spider, unless he was introduced to the binocular at the Chinese factory?

Rather than answer my query the manufacturer simply returned the binocular 'cleaned and repaired'. The pristine nature of the bodywork belied the fact that this was actually a replacement binocular. To this day I wonder whether the manufacturer kept the binocular to see if the spider could survive inside, nourished by some mysterious food source. Perhaps even to this day, this particular binocular is mounted in some board room as a reminder of the need for stringent quality control at the point of production. Or perhaps, a Chinese binocular technician is still quietly chortling to himself, thinking of the British birder that nurtured the tiny spider's egg that he slipped inside a binocular one dull afternoon.

BB

In recent years a number of books on 'fieldcraft' have appeared for birdwatchers. Some of these have contained guidance on the observation strategies that should be used when looking for birds – scanning carefully along hedges, telegraph wires and the muddy edge of lakes for example. All these rely on the best binocular a birdwatcher can afford, so they usually save up as much money as they can in order to buy the highest quality optics possible.

Birdwatchers sometimes customise their binoculars to make them easier to use. For example, Dutch birder and binocular enthusiast Renze de Vries has used short sections of rubber from bicycle inner-tubes to create his own custom-made

Three stages in the production of Renze de Vries's custom-made rubber eyecups, fashioned from bicycle inner-tubes

IMAGES: RENZE DE VRIES

eyecups that suit his eyes perfectly. Another example comes in the form of the various sizes of rubber O-ring which the author uses to position push-up eyecups to suit the anatomy of his eye-sockets (the Bushnell Custom 6x25 binocular illustrated on page XX has been treated in this way).

While the celebrity sponsorship of optics is not a new phenomenon, it gathered pace as rival companies used every conceivable tactic to bring them a commercial edge. Though celebrated British birdwatcher (and former member of comic trio *The Goodies*) Bill Oddie wrote passionately about his Zeiss 10x40 binocular in his humorous *Little Black Bird Book*, he would soon be a Leitz (and later Leica) man, no doubt lured by attractive financial incentives. It is now scarcely possible to be a TV nature personality without also being the public face of one of the top binocular brands. The potential for a binocular and its prominent logo to appear regularly around the neck of a high profile presenter is too good an opportunity for marketing executives to miss, especially those in the UK reaching out to advert-starved BBC viewers.

Binoculars are, of course, also extremely useful for observing wildlife of other kinds. The author has had wonderful views of deer and other mammals through binoculars, when supposedly on birdwatching trips. The recent emergence of binoculars with extreme close focussing (➡ page 93), has been a particular boon for insect enthusiasts. Those wishing to get close-up views of butterflies and dragonflies – two increasingly popular wildlife subjects – use such binoculars in order to make identification in the field possible without the need for a net. Such is the attraction of binoculars for these insect enthusiasts that books entitled *Butterflies Through Binoculars* and *Dragonflies Through Binoculars* have been published in the USA.

MY BINOCULAR STORY

Giant binoculars

MY FIRST PAIR of binoculars had belonged to my father in law who had used them in the army in Italy during World War II. They had 60 mm objectives, were almost a foot long and were totally unsuitable for birdwatching. Nevertheless, I staggered round with them for at least five years. Their size regularly prompted comments on the theme of 'My binoculars are better than yours…'. On a boat to Skomer in the late 1960s an elderly gentleman got very excited explaining that despite their size, my binoculars could not be as good as his, as with his from Morecambe Bay he could tell the time on Fleetwood clock. Ever since, family mythology has regarded this as the criterion for a decent pair of binoculars.

Felicity Pollard

MY BINOCULAR STORY

THANKS FOR THE great glasses (bought from you on eBay in August). I used them on my trip to Yellowstone National Park and they got me in to a bit of trouble. The glasses were so bright, we were able to linger watching three grizzly bears and a pack of five wolves joust over a bison carcass just 200 metres away from us as the sun set. As the light diminished, people started to leave the hillside that we were watching from. Through the binocular, I could still see the action in the low light so we continued to watch. When we decided to leave, we found that everybody had already left the hillside, including the park rangers! We were now about 300 metres from our car, it was dark and there were five wolves and three grizzly bears in the area. We made it out OK and now we have a great story to tell!

Chris Morelle

LANDMARK BINOCULAR: THE PENTAX PAPILIO

Up-close and personal

PENTAX PROVIDED AN important breakthrough in 2005 with its extreme close-focussing papilio model. Available in two magnifications (x6.5 and x8.5) the Papilio's unique feature was to maintain comfortable viewing even at distances as close as 50 cm from the observer, thanks to a unique image convergence system known as CLOSE – Convergent Lens Optical System Engineering. Other advanced features includes the use of aspherical lens elements to improve edge-to-edge sharpness of the image. The Papilio also incorporates a tripod socket, allowing the binocular to be turned in to something approaching a binocular microscope for extreme close-up work.

The Pentax Papilio created quite a stir when it first appeared on the market, especially for those with an interest in insect observation. It was described as 'the most exciting development in binoculars since the invention of phase-coating' in a posting on the leading internet site www.birdforum.net. The Papilio has also been hailed as 'a model that works flawlessly, is wonderfully engineered and constructed and truly deserves to be called a bargain at their low selling price'. One reviewer said that he would be prepared to pay £250 for them – rare praise indeed for what is essentially an ingeniously-designed, but mass-produced Chinese binocular.

As is suggested by its name the Papilio has been eagerly snapped by up butterfly lovers, as well as those wishing to identify insects such as dragonflies while in the field. Pentax has managed to garner such a dedicated following as there is currently no competitor for Papilio. Its handy size has also meant that many birdwatchers have chosen it as their travel binocular, also using the close focussing facility to get detailed views of subjects while away from home.

'I gazed into the clear pools of water at the edge of the river with my Papilios. It was like monsters from the deep – strange and extraordinary creatures came into view and I thought twice about dipping my toes in the water.'

Alex Gilbert

TECHNICAL SPECIFICATION

PENTAX PAPILIO 6.5x21
Field of view: 7.5° (131m at 1,000m)
Apparent field: 48.7°
Exit pupil diameter: 3.2 mm
Weight: 290 g

TECHNICAL SPECIFICATION

PENTAX PAPILIO 8.5x21
Field of view: 6.0° (105 at 1,000m)
Apparent field: 51°
Exit pupil diameter: 2.5 mm
Weight: 290 g

MY BINOCULAR STORY

A lifetime of binoculars

BINOCULARS ARE FASCINATING: not quite, perhaps, grabbing the birdwatcher in the way that floats, flies and assorted tackle become so addictive to the angler; nor, even, quite so likely to start a lengthy conversation as the photographer's gadgets: but definitely exerting a magnetic attraction. After all, beyond a bird guide or two, they are the birdwatcher's only essential equipment, and getting, or dreaming of, the best that can be afforded becomes an ambition.

My early recollections of binoculars revolve around little grey and white Barr & Stroud and Wray adverts in *Bird Notes*, the RSPB's small magazine current when I first joined as a schoolboy. The 'Wray 11' particularly appealed, because of the rather sleek shape and the texture of the black finish – and something about the name. At that time in the 1960s it was easy to 'buy British', too, and they were likely to be as good as any. An uncle, who also had a brass and brown-leather telescope, boasted Ross binoculars and a more experienced birdwatching cousin used Ross 9x35 Stepruvas (as did the inimitable Richard Richardson).

When I began to become serious about birds, taking over gradually from the unsuccessful pursuit of fish, my parents saw the need for binoculars and my father initially borrowed some from a workmate: old, Second World War 7x50 naval ones, complete with cross hairs and some sort of degree scale engraved deep inside. They were large, but not over heavy, and the brilliance of the image, even towards dusk, remains a vivid memory. They had a curious, but not unpleasant, brassy smell, too. If I remember right, they suffered from a lack of a central focussing wheel, requiring separate adjustments of both eyepieces, but their depth of field was such that this was not too much of an inconvenience.

First purchases

We then followed up an ad in a local paper and drove from our home near Lichfield in Staffordshire to a house somewhere towards Birmingham, to buy a pair of 10x50 binoculars. Of the same basic shape as so many Porro prism 10x50s, to look at they could have been Zeiss Jenas, but in fact they were heavy, relatively basic and probably not of the best quality – but they did the job perfectly well and set me up for a while. We did at least know enough to resist the adverts for binoculars that could 'let you walk amongst the craters of the Moon', or with a massive 'zoom in' power, the kind of thing any birdwatcher should avoid.

These early binoculars came to grief, sadly, somewhere on a West Highland hillside – was it Beinn Eighe or Stac Polly? Wherever, I slipped and fell and lost my grip on them – why I didn't have the strap around my neck at that moment I don't know (it is something I always do) but anyway, they rolled end over end down the hill, by some miracle not breaking any exterior lenses but splintering a prism and knocking things out of alignment. I remember the helpless feeling well, as I shouted 'Oh no!' watching them go down a grassy slope, drawn inevitably to a final crunch against a rock.

Next came a finer pair (I find it hard not to say 'pair' although I'm told 'binocular' in the singular is the correct word) – Wray 8x30s, looking very like the more famous Zeiss Jena Deltrintems (which I knew about then, or soon afterwards, from reading Desmond Netherpole-Thomson's favourable words about them somewhere). These were very small and neat: indeed, almost too short, as my fingers forever seemed to creep over the objective lenses. But they came in a lovely tan-brown leather case, with a rich smell that still haunts me. For many years I used these exclusively, until one day, after returning from Gower to Swansea on a bus, I realised they were no longer with me. Surely I could not have been so stupid, so careless, as to leave them upstairs on a double-decker? Frantic phone calls to the bus company failed to recover them and that was that – the end of my British-made binoculars. It was a difficult thing to admit to my parents.

Trading up

Somehow, no doubt with my father's usual support, I scrambled together enough money to replace them and this time I looked through the brochures from adverts in *BIRDS* magazine and decided on my first choice. I can't recall what swayed me towards Zeiss Jena, then, but I liked the look of a new model, subtly different, more rounded, more modern looking, compared with the usual Porro prisms. They looked great on the page. Roof prisms were far beyond my means at this stage. So, I bought some Zeiss Jena 7x40 Septarems, again in a sweet-smelling leather case with red velvet lining. They were wide-angle, and also, early in the game, had retractable eyecups for spectacle wearers. I didn't wear spectacles and this feature didn't appeal, but the binoculars looked so good that it didn't really matter. Sadly, in non-spectacle mode, the eyecups had to be pulled out, and they

proved large, solid and long – not only ideal receptacles for dust and breadcrumbs, but grossly overbalancing the binoculars when hung around my neck. They swung from side to side when I walked along, and so the objective lens was so badly tilted inwards by the overbalancing eyecups that the special coating wore away along one side – I did have the coating re-done but it wore off again quite soon.

Nevertheless, I remember well the magic of these binoculars when I first used them fresh out of the box: I said that even looking at some nearby grass stems, waving in the sun, was a joy. My birdwatching mate, Peter Garvey, said that was probably about as much as we would usually see anyway. They were stunningly good, optically. Now and then, I still use them, just for the pleasure of it. Big and very wide in the hand, they made a great, heavy lump, but the image was beautifully crisp and extraordinarily bright: unbeatable almost. Being so very wide, they also gave a remarkably strong 3D effect, lost by the modern narrow models whose objective lenses are so close together. Even when I later graduated to Leitz 10x40 Trinovids, I was reluctant to

give up the optical quality of the Jenas – but x7 was a bit too low a magnification for many purposes. Even so, I watched estuary birds around Gower and Swansea, and the big Staffordshire reservoirs, for years with them and, as they focussed almost onto my feet, I could watch butterflies and study flowers, too: my binoculars and I became inseparable.

I tried 10x50 Porro prism models and even went so far as to buy some after that, but could never get on with their bulk, the poor position of the focusing wheel and the very shallow eyecups – I always liked to ram the eyecups hard into my eye sockets, partly to reduce the light from the side, partly for greater stability. After several trials, I went for the 10x40 Leitz Trinovid roof prisms, at much-reduced sale price. This was at a time when they were made in Portugal: I recall my dismay when I looked into them through the objective lenses and found fingerprints all over the inners. They went back, and were replaced, but I never felt they were quite the real deal, somehow.

They were undeniably light and small – remarkably neat and easy on the hands – but their rubber eyecups wore badly and soon twisted, and the worst feature was the lack of close focussing: I often had to back away to look at a bird with them.

Rob's trusty Zeiss Septarem 7x40

IMAGE: ROB HUME

MY BINOCULAR STORY *Continued*

But for years these did sterling work. Optically they were great, except in certain circumstances. I could never get rid of a bit of blue and red distortion along thin twigs against a bright sky: and, looking at ducks on a lake, I always found a band of colour distortion – usually tan-brown – along the water's edge. Compared with Zeiss Dialyts, they seemed to have a slightly different quality of image, somehow less perfectly 'flat'.

Newer offerings

On one occasion, I attended the launch of a huge new Zeiss binocular, with a gyroscopic stabilising system. The first pair had gone to the famous BBC television horse-racing commentator, Peter O'Sullevan. They magnified 20 times and were enormously heavy, but Zeiss laid on an interesting little demonstration. We all looked at a newspaper with 6x30, then 8x30, then 10x50 binoculars and, surprisingly, could read it as well from a distance with the x6 as with the x10 binocular. It was all a matter of stability: trembling hands (I suffer badly) combined with breathing, heartbeat and external environmental factors, such as passing traffic, created a constant vibration that made a really sharp image simply impossible – so the greater magnification did nothing to reveal more detail, it just gave a bigger version of the same blurry image. The stabilising binoculars, from much farther away, made everything clear and reading the paper was suddenly easy. But they were gigantic, with a price tag to match.

I was later offered a pair of the newer shape 10x42 Leica Trinovids. The old name Leitz had gone (a pity: Zeiss users had stickers proclaiming 'Zeiss birders do it for a lark' and I always thought 'Real birders do it with their Leitz on' was better, but that became outdated). These were, by comparison with the earlier Leitz, big and heavy, with long, raised strips along the body that hurt my hands – but they focussed much closer and optically were superb, except, still, for a tiny bit of colour fringing on twigs against a white sky. It was odd, really, for such a good and expensive make. But they were good and did me very well.

Coming home

Now, though, I have reconverted to Zeiss: my 10x42 Zeiss Victorys are the best I've had to date, very lightweight, easy to hold, with a beautiful image, albeit with a bit of an insubstantial plastic feel about the body and eyecups. They have seen a good many birds, quite a few Grand Prix, many air shows, a few Rolling Stones concerts and the insides of a number of big cathedrals: in short, I use them for all manner of things. Using good binoculars like this remains a great joy.

Rob Hume

Rob is one of the UK's most respected birdwatching experts and authors

IMAGE: MARCELLA HUME

SEARCHING FOR BUTTERFLIES

I HAVE ALWAYS been interested in all aspects of natural history, particularly butterflies, moths and birds. As a schoolboy in the 1950s, I first tried a pair of Zeiss West 8x30s and was amazed at the clarity and field of view. A kind local optician who stocked binoculars allowed me to try them from his front shop door. Prior to that, the best binoculars I had tried were a pair of Ross Enbecco 13x60 – again through kindness of the manager of the Midland Bank who was a keen butterfly enthusiast too. At the time he was the treasurer of the Entomologists' Record. That's how my schoolboy friend and I came to know him as we both subscribed. Those Zeiss were a virtually unaffordable £50 even in those far away days and it was to be over ten years later before I could afford to buy a pair of the new Zeiss West 10x50s which I purchased in 1970. I negotiated a decent discount, of around 30% if I remember correctly, but even so they still cost me a month's salary. I visited most of the broadleaf woodlands in central and southern England, specifically searching for my favourite butterfly – the purple emperor. That search was quite successful as I turned it up in a number of woods which even today still have good populations. Binoculars enable me to find and identify species which would otherwise pass unseen, especially by scanning trees and shrubs for 'hidden' butterflies. As a by-product of my searches, I also found some interesting birds, not least a honey buzzard and Montagu's harrier.

John McFeely

'I made use of my Nikon 10x42 SE last week in a memorable observation. I managed to watch a bat in flight for some time as it swooped and fluttered about searching for insects. It was fairly close, perhaps 50 to 100 feet, and a fantastic sight in the binocular. However, I am unable to identify which family of the order Chiroptera was in view.' PETER ABRAHAMS

The eyes of the hunter

Those with a desire to shoot birds and other animals, rather than just watch them, also have a need for binoculars. Binoculars allow hunters to find their quarry, successfully identify the species found and make key distance judgements. In some countries hunters make up a very significant proportion of the people buying binoculars, and in the 1950s and 1960s they were the principal customer of the US company Bushnell.

The main attributes of a hunting binocular are good light gathering power (as much hunting is done at dawn or dusk) and a reasonably wide field. Such specifications as 7x50, 8x56 and 9x63 have thus proved particularly popular with the hunting fraternity, and the more modern roof prism models come with the added benefit of waterproofing and the streamlined, space-saving shape that this prism arrangement confers. Roof prism models are somewhat easier to use in confined spaces than their Porro prism counterparts. Some models are clearly targeted at the hunting market, with the emergence in recent years of camouflage-bodied versions of the standard range from makers such as Bushnell.

HRH Prince Charles wearing his Zeiss 10x25 binocular during a hunting trip in the mountains

'As a hunter, you have more need for optical aids than any other outdoor enthusiast – the proper light binocular, a dependable riflescope, and often a spotting scope in stalking and locating elusive wild game.' HENRY PAUL

Binoculars – especially Porro prism models – provide the three dimensional effect that gunsights simply cannot replicate, enabling the user to judge the relative position and distance of targets. Writing in his book *Binoculars and All Purpose Telescopes*, Henry Paul shares his concern of occasionally seeing fellow hunters carefully examining him with the telescopic sight of their rifles, trying to ascertain his antler or horn length! He admits that he would much rather they use binoculars to separate hunter from prey.

MY BINOCULAR STORY

Binoculars for hunting

I BOUGHT MY Docter 8x50 Nobilem binoculars in 1998. I used them for wildlife observation and deer stalking. I chose them for their clarity and light gathering ability, as I used binoculars a lot at dawn and dusk. They were returned for servicing after they misted up, caused by being caught out in the Scottish hills, miles from home, in the worst downpour I've ever experienced. I could hardly

see 6 feet in front of me! I changed the binos for Docter Optic 8x32 aspherical in 2003. These are also excellent and were chosen due to the smaller physical size and weight reduction compared to the 8x50s. I wanted smaller (but good quality) binos as I was then involved in deer stalking over much rougher/steeper ground than previously and every ounce tells after a few miles. The downside is less light gathering ability at dawn and dusk, but they are still good binos. I've just upgraded again and left the Docter Optik camp and defected to Leica but only because the new Leica Geovid (8x42) has an in-built laser range finder. They're expensive but optically brilliant and I find the range finder very useful.

British hunter

'A hare is sitting on a lea,
Which, he feels certain, none can see.
But, armed with Zeisses of great strength,
Assiduously and at some length,
A man from a commanding height,
Surveys the tiny spoon-eared wight,
Quite unaware that, from on high,
A God serenely views the spy.'
Christian Morgenstern

A binocular-clad hunter shows off his deer kill on a pre-1950s American hunting trip

the **better** to see with, my dear

Weeks and weeks of planning went into this hunting trip, with special care given to selecting your equipment. One item you were sure to include was your new Bausch & Lomb Zephyr-Light Binocular . . . for you knew then as you do now the importance of a binocular capable of bringing out the detail of far-off objects, even in poor light.

Back home, you'll find sporting events, a day at the beach or a drive into the country much more enjoyable, for you'll see better and more clearly with your Bausch & Lomb Binocular. When you buy a B&L Binocular, you pay for the world's best . . . and get it. There's a booklet to tell you all about it; write Bausch & Lomb Optical Co., 10034 Lomb Park, Rochester 2, New York.

from $192.50

BAUSCH & LOMB

SINCE 1853

FIELD & STREAM OCTOBER 1958   97

Hunters are a key user group for binoculars, and as this 1958 advertisement suggests, good low light performance is a key criterion in their selection. Although hunting tends to be a male-dominated pastime in much of the developed world, here we see what is presumably a husband and wife team enjoying a special trip

LANDMARK BINOCULAR: THE LEICA GEOVID

LANDMARK BINOCULAR

Range and vision

LEICA MADE AN important step forward in optical design with its highly innovative Geovid II binocular which was launched in its 2004. The first high-performance binocular to feature an integrated laser range-finding device, the Geovid II has proved extremely popular with hunters, giving them a highly accurate readout of the distance of potential targets up to 1,200 away. Special forces and law enforcement officers have also made use of this technically-advanced binocular and it has seen limited use on the golf course, helping golfers and their caddies to determine the distance to the hole, so that appropriate club choices can be made.

One of the key advances of the Geovid II was its ability to maintain the operational qualities of a normal binocular, despite harbouring some highly specialised electronic components. It is lightweight, has a central hinge and central focussing and although the LED range-finder is included it does not interfere with the optics to a noticeable degree. Before its introduction, it was only possible to make large, heavy range-finding binoculars. They also used transparent LCD displays in the optical path, that reduce light transmission by about 40%.

Range information in the Geovid II – which is available in 8x42, 8x56, 10x42 and 15x56 configurations – is made available by depressing a button on the upper body of the binocular which yields a small LED rectangle, and the distance of the object in it is projected in figures into the optical path below. When not used in range-finding mode, the Geovid II operates like a conventional binocular and is no larger than many standard roof prism instruments. The Geovid II features an aluminium die-cast housing to reduce weight, is filled with nitrogen to prevent internal fogging and is waterproof.

Leica's Geovid II binocular is heavily patented in the Europe and USA and it took several years for rival companies (notably Zeiss) to launch parallel products.

The Geovid II was not just a design triumph for Leica – its strong sales also helped to improve the financial standing of the company at a time when its future had been uncertain. This has no doubt been helped by the availability of a version which displays the distance in yards instead of metres, for those countries which do not use the metric system.

'The models with the 42mm front lens diameter not only combine the "observation" with the "rangefinding" functions to optical and electronic perfection – their handiness makes them eminently suitable for the world's great variety of hunting adventures.'

Leica brochure

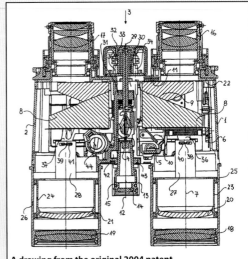

A drawing from the original 2004 patent application for the Geovid II binocular

IMAGE: LEICA CAMERA AG, SOLMS, GERMANY

TECHNICAL SPECIFICATION

LEICA GEOVID 8X42
Field of view: 7° (125m at 1,000 m)
Apparent field: 56°
Exit pupil diameter: 5.3 mm
Weight: 950 g (including batteries)

6 Let me entertain you

Renoir's famous painting *La Loge* (The Theatre Box; painted in 1874) shows a well-attired couple nestled in their seats in a smart theatre auditorium. We do not know the name of the performance they are watching, but our eyes are drawn to the binoculars they are holding in their hands. The lady, complete with an impressive costume redolent of the late 1800s, has her binoculars ready for peering down at the stage, where she is currently gazing. But why, we wonder, is the smart-suited gentleman looking up, across the auditorium? Who has he spotted in the audience, what clandestine activities does this suggest and how will this particular story end? For over a hundred years binoculars have been taken to the theatre by those wanting to get a close look at the action on – and off – the stage. In more modern times they have been a valuable tool when watching sporting activities from afar. This chapter explains more about their use by people to add enjoyment to live events and other leisure pursuits outside the arena of nature. It includes the intriguing story of how a famous name from the early history of binoculars is kept alive on a football field in Germany.

Binoculars can bring enjoyment to a whole range of leisure activities

Opera glasses found favour owing to their small size and often decorative nature

THE REASON THAT binoculars have become such popular consumer items is surely because they have such a wide range of possible uses. During research for the book the author scoured through a range of marketing brochures and noted at least 30 different stated uses for binoculars. While the benefits of binoculars for nature observation clearly attract many buyers – as discussed in the previous chapter – they can also be used to enhance the enjoyment of a host of other hobbies and interests.

'I have always had a pair of binoculars in my car. A pair has always been in my work bag. I think they are one of the most useful and beautiful instruments to have.'
MICHAEL KACZOR

A Bakelite binocular from a London theatre

It would not be surprising if simple Galilean opera or theatre glasses turned out to be the most common binocular found in homes across the Western world. They are less expensive than prismatic binoculars, have few mechanical parts to go wrong and above all do their job remarkably well. These simple instruments were produced in their millions and were used mainly by those attending live performances.

During the Victorian era in the UK it became fashionable for family members to be photographed with objects that suggested something of their social status. This photograph from about 1910, taken in Scotland, shows two ladies, one holding a book (suggesting she could read) and another holding a Galilean binocular. Binoculars would have been a luxury item at this time, with a price that made them affordable only to the most well-to-do members of society

Ross was one of a number of British firms that used sporting associations to help sell its binocular range. In this advertisement from 1956 the firm also mentions the British navy's use of Ross instruments to add to the allure of its brand. The author is not certain that the bold statement concerning the outstanding brightness of Ross binoculars was established in scientifically rigorous conditions, as it is not borne out by modern-day tests

Many ways to use a binocular

Air traffic control
Alpine rescue services
Astronomy
Aviation
Birdwatching
Botanical study
Camping
Climbing
Coastguard stations
Construction
Entomology
Exploration
Fishing

Game keeping
Hiking
Holidays
Horse-racing
Hunting
Mammal watching
Marine rescue services
Meteorology
Military use
Mountaineering
Navigation
Opera
Plane spotting

Research purposes
Shipping
Supervision of large
building sites
Surveillance
Theatre
Touring by car
Train spotting
Travelling
Watching space launches
Watching sport
Yachting

Notes from the author's research showing the range of possible uses for binoculars as given in marketing brochures. Some seem more sensible than others – the author has never quite understood how binoculars are integral to camping!

This inexpensive Bushnell Olympic 7x35 'Medallist 84' is in a completely different optical league to the Leitz binocular pictured overleaf. It was made for the Los Angeles games of 1984. The instruction booklet for this binocular reads, 'They boldly and permanently display the traditional ring symbol of the Olympics, as well as the "Star in Motion" marking, which officially identify them with the 23rd Olympiad'

Fans of popular British singer Robbie Williams could watch his 2007 performances through a specially branded binocular. After the concerts these binoculars became collectable in their own right

"**What a play!**"

CARL ZEISS BINOCULARS

Modern football is a fast, open game—you need a binocular with a wide field of view to follow the players with ease, and to really see the "team work."

Carl Zeiss Binoculars have an extremely wide field of view, and exceptionally sharp definition—you can actually see the expressions on the players' faces.

Ask your dealer to show you the various Carl Zeiss models.

Write for literature.

 CARL ZEISS, Inc., 485 Fifth Ave., New York
728 South Hill Street, Los Angeles

Followers of American football in the 1930s were encouraged to get close in to the action through the purchase of a binocular, in this Zeiss advertisement from the period. Later the company of US businessman David Bushnell would popularise the use of binoculars at American football games with a range of purpose-built models. The Rose Bowl Commission always bought 100 binoculars from his company for the famous New Year's Day game and gave him six seats on the 50 yard line

While the low cost resulted in widespread ownership, some were instruments of beauty modelled in gold, mother of pearl or ivory and were clearly designed to impress others as much as get one closer to the stage. Most models are small enough to be tucked into the pocket or purse when not in use. As well as allowing the user to study the facial features and costumes of the performers, binoculars – often clandestinely – also enabled one to observe other members of the audience.

This special 1972 Olympic edition of the Leitz 7x35B Trinovid could possibly be the rarest commercially-marketed Trinovid binocular in existence. Just 200 examples of this model were produced (along with 600 Olympic 8x32s and 200 of the 10x40 model) to commemorate the 1972 Munich Olympic Games. This was the Leitz Trinovid's only special edition and this example, marked 001, was apparently ordered and shipped directly from Leitz to the late James A. Collins, an American industrial engineer, based in Hong Kong. Collins was a collector of all things Leica and amassed over 1,800 pieces

'A suitable opera glass or low-power wide-field binocular imparts box seat effectiveness to a gallery position.' HENRY PAUL

During the height of theatre going before the invention or widespread ownership of the television, many theatres would even provide simple opera glasses for hire for a few pennies. Some are still available on the backs of seats in ageing auditoria.

The advent of large coloured screens, with instant replays of key moments of action, seems to have put paid to the use of binoculars by the majority of people attending major sporting events, such as football, rugby and cricket matches. Indeed, the use of a binocular can even raise eyebrows at many sporting events today, especially in the male-dominated world of Premiership football. The author's use of a compact binocular to follow the distant action provoked repeated puzzled looks from fellow supporters the year he had a season ticket at Leeds United Football Club.

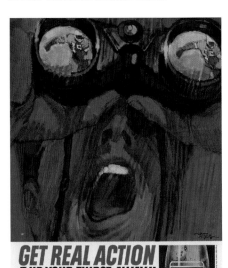

A dramatic advertisement from 1964 for the popular US drink 7-Up, using the theme of an American football match reflected in the objective lenses of a binocular to convey the sense of excitement at a game

A 1989 programme commemorating an important match for Carl Zeiss Jena Football Club. A prize draw held during the game provided the lucky winner with…a Carl Zeiss Jena binocular of course!

The elegant attire of the young French woman pictured in this New Year Card from 1921 suggests she may be at the races, where her (probably Huet) binocular would be invaluable. Research points to the fact that the person featured is a noted film actress of the period

Binoculars are extremely useful at the races. Here a young woman uses a binocular with considerable heritage to add enjoyment to her visit to York racecourse. The binocular in question is a scarce 1920s Zeiss Delactis 8x40 model which was originally owned by a Lady Ganzoni of Ipswich. The Ganzonis were a wealthy family who no doubt attended meetings at Ipswich race course. The binocular may have been given to Lady Ganzoni and her husband as a wedding present

On the other side of the Atlantic binoculars have for many years been used by spectators watching another kind of football – that played by men wearing protective helmets and padded clothing. Marketeers have tried to tap into this interest with advertisements stressing the benefits of their binoculars for sporting uses, especially those with a wide-angle of view. Others have used binoculars to promote the sales of other products consumed during sporting events, such as drinks.

The sponsorship of the football team in Jena, East Germany by the firm Carl Zeiss means that the name of this famous binocular maker lives on long after the company ceased to trade. Future adventures in European football competitions may once again bring the name of Carl Zeiss Jena alive for those in the west.

The race course is one of the few sporting arenas where people can still regularly be seen using a binocular. Even here though, live pictures on the big screen of galloping horses mean that binoculars are surely less commonly used than in the past.

'Boat racing, auto racing, horse racing, or almost any other form of fast sport is much more fun for the observer owning a good pair of glasses'   HENRY PAUL

Horse-racing events covered on television allowed the author as a child to see which models were used by the British royal family, since they were one of the few occasions when royalty could be seen using their binoculars. He found it

BINOCULAR WITH A HISTORY

Great Uncle's horse-racing binoculars

MY GREAT UNCLE owned a Swift 7x35 Panoramic binocular which he used when he went horse racing. He spent a year not working and financed himself through low level bets at the races ('beating the bookies' as he called it!) and these were an investment for that purpose. He was quite hard up all his life, but liked to have the best, when he could afford it – he had a Leica camera as well.

Daphne

The Swift Panoramic 7x35 was one of the premium wide-angle binoculars of the 1960s and 1970s. It retailed for £39.50 in 1973

A HORSE CALLED BINOCULAR

DURING 2008 A four-year-old horse with a very appropriate name for readers of this book burst onto the racing scene. Such was the success of the horse leading up to the famous meeting at Cheltenham that one *Sporting Life* headline reporting a victory read 'Rivals need binoculars'. Although the horse was actually beaten into second place in the extreme novices' hurdle at Cheltenham, it bounced back to win another important race for novices at the home of the Grand National – Aintree. His rider at Aintree, Tony McCoy, described binocular as a 'classy horse'.

The celebrity sponsorship of binoculars has a long tradition. This 1951 advertisement provides a visually impressive platform for a popular television presenter to recommend a specific model by British manufacturer Kershaw. It is not known how lucrative such endorsements were at this time for figures in the public eye

RIGHT: Some manufacturers pitched products at just one segment of the market. This 1950s advertisement for the 'Newmarket ladies' glass', is an early attempt to attract female buyers to a specific model

FAR RIGHT: A Kentucky whiskey producer uses a horse-racing theme to market its tipple

This binocular-shaped limited edition drinking flask commemorates a special event in British racing history. On 28 September 1996 Italian jockey Lanfranco (known as Frankie) Dettori went 'through the card' at the Ascot Racing festival by riding seven winners out of seven mounts during the day. The names and odds of the seven winning horses are engraved on one of the binocular barrels. Only 350 examples of this flask were made

Racing events give sponsors the opportunity to bring wider brand awareness through the issuing of complimentary binoculars. Featured here is a folding binocular provided at York races by the rail company GNER, together with a clever Australian instrument in the shape of a beer can, with the words 'backing the Melbourne cup'

rather satisfying when he eventually identified the Queen's race-course binocular as a Leitz 8x32 roof prism model – top of the range at the time of course!

At several major race courses in the UK a World War II stand-mounted 10x80 binocular can still be used to follow the race from a high balcony in the main stand. One instrument can be regularly seen on Channel 4 Television's racing programme, as one of the reporters takes up his position in front of this magnificent instrument.

Fashion is a key part of attending horse-racing events in the UK and being seen with a high quality binocular clearly complements some people's sartorial choices. The author has seen eBay listings for vintage Zeiss Jena 7x50 models (a classic race going configuration, ➧ page 120) in their luxurious and sweet-smelling leather cases, encouraging readers to purchase a binocular that 'provides so much more of a statement at the races than cheap compact binoculars'.

We can only imagine what symbolism lies behind this early 20th century Spanish postcard of a bathing costumed woman peering high into the sky through a binocular, while standing on the edge of a diving board

'The selection of the binocular best adapted to your needs requires some thought beforehand, and a certain knowledge of what to expect from a particular model, if you are to get the best results. After all, I can't go on a racecourse and expect to know all the colours of the horses in any particular race unless I've done a bit of homework first'. RAYMOND GLENDENNING

A unique event occurred on an American horse-racing track in 1924 when a horse called Zeiss won two events thanks to the riding skills of 2nd Lt. Ahnlund. Visitors to the event could enjoy the unparalleled sight through their Zeiss binocular of a horse called Zeiss winning a race for which the winning prize was – amazingly – a Zeiss binocular!

So-called 'spectacle binoculars' bring enjoyment and fun to sporting events at home and outdoors

Sporting commentators on television and radio still find a use for binoculars, as they keep track of positions and plays and relate these to the audience. For example, the author has seen BBC TV commentators positioned behind ranks of computer screens at athletics events, but still equipped with Canon stabilised binoculars to follow the action in real time.

Some manufacturers have made a concerted effort to appeal to the sporting segment of the market. Companies such as Swift produced models named 'Sport King' and 'Panoramic' in the 1960s and 1970s, and such binoculars often included associated sporting icons on their bodies or supporting photographs on the boxes. Other manufacturers tried to suggest specific sporting uses for their binoculars, with perhaps the most unusual being the wide-angle 7x21 'Bullfight' model produced in the 1960s by the Japanese company Eikow. In recent years Bushnell has sought to reignite interest in the value of binoculars at sporting events through their extreme wide-angle binocular range. Their 4x21 model in particular, with its field of view of 900 feet at 1,000 yards, certainly produces impressive wide-angle views of the action.

Spectators using binoculars at athletics events in the 1970s and 1980s could sometimes zoom in and see sponsorship badges on the tracksuits of German competitors. This example even manages to incorporate some humour

'Modern football is a fast, open game – you need a binocular with a wide field of view to follow the players with ease, and to really see the "team work". Carl Zeiss binoculars have an extremely wide field of view, and exceptionally sharp definition – you can actually see the expressions on the players' faces.'

ZEISS ADVERTISEMENT (1931)

A special category of binocular device is an instrument that actually perches on the observer's nose and ears like a spectacle. These were originally advertised for use watching sport and other live events – the model made by the English firm Kershaw even bearing the name 'Sportsman'. Alex and Will Gilbert, from Harrogate, own an example of such a binocular; she uses it at the races, he for getting close-up action of events on his home television!

People *participating* in sport also benefit from using binoculars and other optical aids. The author was contacted by an English small-bore rifle competitor who used a Leica Duovid 10-15x50 binocular to see where targets had been hit at a range of 50 and 100 yards. This particular user found the binocular of immense use when teaching young shooters their craft, even though a mounted tripod is usually the instrument of choice for shooters. The fact that he also had a second home in the south of France, not far from the Pyrenees, meant that the binocular found a use – tripod mounted – during holiday times to view eagles and vultures circling over the Pic de Bugarach.

The fiancée of acclaimed ocean swimmer Ben Lecomte first caught sight of him through a binocular in the waters off the French coast, after his record-breaking 3,716 mile trans-Atlantic swim in 1998

The Beijing 2008 Olympics seemed to represent something of a renaissance for binocular use at sporting events. The die was seemingly cast at the opening ceremony when VIPs, including US President George Bush and Chinese President Hu Jintao, were seen using binoculars, presumably from their goody bags, to get close-up views of the amazing spectacle described as 'the greatest show on earth'. No doubt the meticulous organising team ensured that Chinese models were selected, thereby providing a further powerful statement about the nation's intentions as a major binocular manufacturer. Then, as the dramatic events of the 29th Olympiad unfolded, spectators could be seen using binoculars to watch everything from badminton to beach volleyball. During the 70m women's archery competition, one archer was even seen to be wearing a binocular as she competed, using it to check where each arrow had landed after every attempt. A previous example of binocular use in the Olympics comes from 1992, when Göran Petersson used a Zeiss 20x60 image stabilised binocular to good effect while judging the sailing events in Barcelona, just two years after this special binocular was launched.

Fujinon binoculars have established a loyal following among sailing and boating enthusiasts. Their high quality, rugged Porro prism models are among the best all weather binoculars currently made

'I look down the list of events taking place today – it only takes seconds for my top, journalistic instincts to home in on the big story of the day. I pack my official Olympic merchandise rucksack – sweatband, check; hideous yellow plastic Olympic mac; check. I attach a zoom lens to my camera and pick up a pair of binoculars in the curious miscellany of a shop downstairs in the Media Centre. I'm off to watch some women's beach volleyball and I don't want to miss a minute.'
BRITISH COMEDIAN DOM JOLY

MY BINOCULAR STORY

Ocean wanderers

PETER CHADWICK HAS fond memories of watching sailing boats and ships around the busy port city of Liverpool during his childhood days in the 1950s. Along with his father, he used a variety of different binoculars to study the shipping traffic, including a Ross Stepruva 9x35, which was bought from a Liverpool optician's shop without their case for £28. At this time Liverpool was an important port for passenger and commercial vessels, and the nearby Birkenhead dock

became a breaking ground for U-boats after World War II. Peter remembers hearing that U-boat bridge binoculars were once available from the breaking yard.

Peter used to particularly enjoy spotting the names of the ships and the port of registration on the stern. It was possible to check out in advance the predicted movements of some vessels by studying the *Shipping Times*. Some of his most vivid memories concerned the trans-Atlantic liners that headed out from Liverpool bound for

the USA, including such ships as the RMS Britannic, which in 1960 became the last liner of the celebrated White Star company to make such a crossing. Other noteworthy sightings were the Norwegian whaling ships.

Peter recalls that very few other people watched ships at this time because not many other people owned binoculars. He recalled that this father cherished his binoculars, using them for birdwatching and walking through his life. He even had them in a nursing home when he was 96 years old.

MY BINOCULAR STORY

Binoculars for all uses

I USE BINOCULARS for various purposes, having always been a keen birdwatcher. When I was seven my parents bought me a pair of Rand Royal View 3x30 which I promptly dropped into a swollen brook from my vantage-point on a bridge. It was a Sunday evening and I was, of course, heartbroken. My father and I returned to the scene of this devastating loss the following evening armed with a garden rake. Unbelievably, he salvaged them, perhaps even more so, they worked and continued to do so in perpetuity. I still have them, it's

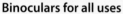

simply a question of where to find them amongst the accumulation of many years' clutter.
In my late teens I enjoyed watching point-to-point races, and so when my 21st birthday arrived a pair of binoculars was a logical and gratefully accepted gift. Whilst I rarely go racing any more I find my Carl Zeiss Jena 7x50 Binoctems very useful because I commentate at a local equestrian cross-country event about eight times a year. Their usefulness is only part of the reason that I derive pleasure from them. Like anything of quality there is simply a delight in the

ownership. For this reason I also have too many (four) Contax cameras, entirely because of their Zeiss lenses.

Perhaps one of the most memorable experiences of my 30 years' of Zeiss use was the view from the 'Roof of Africa'. In 1995 I ascended Kilimanjaro and the vista from nearly 19,500 feet was simply stunning. The clouds were 8,000 feet beneath as we surveyed the scene from the popular viewpoint of Gilman's Point as the sun rose. It was breathtaking, not just metaphorically.

Tom

During the 2008 US Open tennis competition, which eventually saw British player Andy Murray compete in the final against Swiss legend Roger Federer, US comedian Will Ferrell watched Murray's impressive semi-final victory against Spanish ace Rafael Nadal with a Nikon Action binocular close to hand. Sporting Rupert Bear trousers, Ferrell wasted no time in high-fiving Murray after his famous victory that took the Scot to his first Grand Slam final.

The sailing of smaller boats has become a popular pastime in many parts of the world. This has led to the widespread ownership of binoculars for use at sea or on inland lakes and rivers. The instrument of choice is often a 7x50 binocular, but writing in his book *Binocular and All Purpose Telescopes* (1980) Henry Paul suggests that lower power binocular in the x4 to x6 range are often overlooked by small boat owners, despite being useable even when the boat is moving about on the sea surface.

During the 1960s girl scouts in the USA were able to buy their own specially branded binoculars for camping trips

Binoculars are, therefore, part of the standard kit of every sailing enthusiast, even those that never venture out to sea themselves. Individual eyepiece focus models tend to be popular as they are easier to waterproof than centre focus versions and once set by a user for observing boats never need to be changed again. There are a variety of special models aimed at this market, with perhaps most innovative being the models that now incorporate a compass which can be sighted as the observer looks through the binocular.

ABOVE: The author views the Italian Dolomites through coin-operated binoculars from a view-point in the beautiful town of Bassano del Grappa, which gave its name to the popular alcoholic drink 'Grappa', still distilled in the region

LEFT: A Bausch & Lomb binocular advertisement from 1920 aimed at the new breed of automobile owners

COULD BINOCULARS HAVE SAVED THE TITANIC?

A CENTRAL QUESTION for those who have studied the infamous first voyage of the RMS *Titanic* is the matter of whether the disaster might have been avoided. And it seems that the recent sale of a locker key, that should have been on the ship when it left Southampton bound for New York on 10 April 1912, has provided a means to unlock at least one part of the mystery surrounding the sinking of this 46,000 tonne ship.

Strangely, the main figure in the story is a person who did not actually sail on the *Titanic* as it begun its maiden voyage across the Atlantic with over 2,200 people on board – second officer David Blair. Blair had been due to serve on the first trans-Atlantic crossing of the *Titantic* in 1912, but was replaced at the last minute by another officer, owing to personnel changes higher up the command chain. Blair wrote of his disappointment in a postcard to his sister-in-law – 'Am afraid I shall have to step out to make room for chief officer of the *Olympic*. This is a magnificent ship, I feel very disappointed I am not to make her first voyage.' Charles Lightoller, the man who replaced Blair as second officer on board the *Titanic*, was in fact the most senior officer to survive the disaster.

It seems that, preoccupied by tidying up loose ends before departing the ship, it slipped Blair's mind to hand over the key to the locker in the crow's nest which housed a binocular for the designated lookout. This would have been used to see potential dangers in the distance – including icebergs. Instead, the vital key was carried off the ship when he left it in Southampton, having been used by Blair to access the binoculars in the locker on the short voyage from Belfast, Northern Ireland, where the *Titanic* had been built.

Lookout Fred Fleet, who also survived the disaster, told an official enquiry that if they had binoculars they might have seen the iceberg sooner. When asked by a US senator how much sooner it might have been spotted the lookout replied, 'Enough to get out of the way'. Fleet went further and described the key as having the potential to save the *Titanic*.

Sir Ernest Shackleton was called as an expert witness to the *Titanic* enquiry, but disputed the wisdom of using binoculars in such a situation because of the limitations in terms of field of view. He is reported to have said, 'I do not believe in any look-out man having glasses at all.' Instead he believed that this sort of facility should be left to officers who would focus on any important objects sighted by an eyes-only observer. Many commentators actually believe that the fate of the *Titanic* was in the hands of the captain, E.J.Smith, who allowed the ship to go too fast in an ice-field which he had warnings about.

Despite not being able to join the *Titanic* on its first voyage, Blair kept the locker key as a memento and eventually passed it on to his daughter, who in turn gave it to a society for British and international sailors in the 1980s. The key – inscribed with the words 'Crows Nest Telephone, Titanic' – and the accompanying postcard sold for £90,000 in a UK auction in 2007. Just how much would the binocular itself be worth, should it ever reach the surface again?

More than 1,500 people lost their lives in the *Titanic* disaster. While many maritime experts doubt that binoculars could have saved the ship, it seems certain that they will be forever linked to the most infamous of ocean disasters.

Travelling companions

Binoculars make ideal travelling companions, especially on overseas trips where there are so many new things to see. There were many early attempts to appeal to users who wished to take their binoculars on holiday, with 'travelling' being one of the most commonly-suggested uses in pre-World War II catalogues. It is also possible to find postcards, even quite early examples, that show binoculars in use in scenic situations.

The rise in the popularity of the motor car in the USA during the 1920s meant that increasing numbers of people were setting off for weekend excursions in their vehicles. Bausch & Lomb attempted to specifically target this segment of the market with a series of advisements aimed at these 'autoists' as they called them.

'What autoist does not multiply by many times the interest of his tours, when accompanied by his binocular?' BAUSCH & LOMB BINOCULAR ADVERTISEMENT (1920)

It is still quite common to find coin-operated binoculars at tourist destinations which have a good vantage-point, such as mountain peaks and seaside locations. These help people who have not brought their own binocular to get better views while on holiday. Some of these models have stylish designs which can add to the allure of their often dramatic locations.

The wide open vistas made possible by the lofty decks of liners and cruise ships are also very conducive to binocular viewing. Advertisements from the late 19th and early 20th century can be found which stress the value of binoculars on trans-Atlantic voyages and other marine excursions. The first-class decks during these pioneering years of ocean travel would have buzzed with the excitement of new things seen over the waves through binoculars. One of the most intriguing stories concerning binoculars comes from the ill-fated maiden voyage of the Titantic (➤ see box).

I was on a boat trip round Emsworth harbour in Hampshire when I overheard the following conversation. Middle-aged man to older gentleman, 'Would you like to borrow a pair of binoculars?'
Reply, 'No thank you, I'd rather look in the general than the particular'

HEATHER ROWE

Forward-thinking tourist authorities sometimes use binocular imagery to attract holiday makers attracted to destinations with impressive natural history. A series of recent advertisements by the Gibraltar tourist office represent a striking example.

The advent of high quality and waterproof compact models has meant that more and more people seem to be taking their binoculars on holiday – ever conscious as they are of weight restrictions during air travel and the convenience of a pocket binocular once at the holiday destination. Binoculars come in useful

Three postcards featuring binoculars in use by travellers in the USA (1959, left), Hungary (date unknown, top right) and Switzerland (1911, bottom right)

Foreign holidays give binocular uses the opportunity to scan new horizons from fresh vantage-points. Here, the author uses a tripod-mounted binocular to look for golden orioles from the dramatically-located terrace of a rented house in the Cevennes mountains in southern France

WOOD'S

ACHROMATIC BINOCULAR GLASSES.

As supplied to the
ATLANTIC STEAMSHIPS,
THE MERSEY
DOCKS & HARBOUR
BOARD,
THE MILITARY,
&c., &c.

THE NEW
PRICE LIST
IS SENT BY
RETURN POST
ON
APPLICATION.

20, LORD STREET,
LIVERPOOL.

THE "TOURIST," 4½ in. (Closed), 40s.; THE "UNIVERSAL," 4½ in., 65s.;
THE "MILITARY STAFF," 5½ in., £5 15s.

LEFT: Zeiss used testimonials from prominent people to promote their binoculars. Here, Captain Hartley of the SS *Leviathan* of the United States Lines looks through what is most likely a 7x50 Binoctar glass. The ship, originally a German vessel named SS *Vaterland* but seized by the US government in 1917, became a popular trans-Atlantic passenger liner in the 1920s and early 1930s

RIGHT: Early travellers on trans-Atlantic steamships may have used binoculars manufactured by the British company Wood. Their base in Liverpool, one of the country's leading ports at this time, allowed them to take advantage of the numerous ships leaving the UK for foreign shores during the late 19th century

MY BINOCULAR STORY

Alpine binoculars

I AM JUST back from a fortnight trekking in the Tirolean Zillertal Alps. Here I saw several pairs of Swarovski binoculars in use in the mountains. The first was a 7x42 Porro prism model on the window ledge for customer use in an Alpine hut – showing a degree of trust that might surprise city dwellers. I tried it out one evening and was impressed with the edge to edge sharpness and low light capability. Another was perched on the bar in a different hut, for customers to use on request. Then, I was descending from the Olperer group at about 2,200 meters towards Speigeleis See and met a cow on the path, followed by another and then a third. I stepped aside above the path to let the herd pass and noticed that they were escorted by a herdsman and his wife. He was wearing a Tyrolean hat, very old traditional leather trousers, and the most thoroughly worn pair of binoculars I've ever seen – more metal showing than leather! I didn't ask if they were the x7 or x10 model. I also saw several other pairs owned by hut wardens, either Habicht or SLC models. I imagine this suggests a degree of patriotism and also that they're bomb proof.

Jem Coady

for a variety of specialist applications when on holiday. Climbers, for example, are reported to sometimes use binoculars to check the configuration of the rock faces and the presence of crevices, prior to ascending routes. Using binoculars overseas can, however, bring with it certain dangers (▶ see box).

'Traveling without binoculars? You may not be getting the most from your travel money either in pleasure or knowledge. Vacation activity is often outdoor activity where it's sometimes difficult, or impossible, to get as close to objects of interest as you'd like – so bring them to you.'
HENRY PAUL

There is nothing worse than a headache to interfere with... the view through your binoculars! (A 1950s advertisement from the USA)

Varied uses

The author spent his teenage years in suburban Manchester. The proximity of Ringway Airport, as it was then known, which was just a short bus ride from his home in Stockport, meant that many of his childhood friends were keen aircraft spotters. Binoculars were perhaps the key part of any plane spotter's equipment at this time. He remembers at school how on Monday morning his friends would tell of the special aircraft that had been sighted at Ringway over the weekend. A particular flutter of excitement concerned a rare Luxair cargo plane that had apparently not been seen in the north of England before. Finances were pretty tight for many families in this part of England at the time, and binoculars were frequently borrowed off grandparents or older relatives to be used on the viewing platforms at Ringway. Since this time, Ringway airport has grown into the UK's largest air hub outside London in the form of Manchester Airport. In 2007 it handled over 22 million passengers and the

Two green-fingered ladies use their binoculars to study the detail of Brodsworth Hall gardens in Yorkshire

MY BINOCULAR STORY

Spying on the Maoists

IN 1977 I bought a pair of East German Carl Zeiss Jena 8x30 binoculars specifically for birdwatching. I used them extensively, not least because my 33-year career in the Royal Navy took me all over the world. As a result of continued use I became very attached to them and normally wouldn't leave home without them.

In October 2004 I, along with my wife, joined a local Weymouth group on a walking trip to Nepal. The aim of the trip was to 'experience' Nepal and trek in the Annapurna mountain region.

Having spent two days in Kathmandu we travelled by coach to Pokhara and set off on our adventure. After two nights we were leaving the village of Ghorepani (3,000m) heading for Tadapani, when we were halted on the trail by a very earnest looking young Maoist requesting that we were required to each pay a fee in order to be able to continue on our way.

As our guide was sorting out payment, most of our group carried on up the trail but the Maoist spotted my binoculars and said that I had to hand them over as they could have been used against the Maoists in the hills. A prolonged discussion took place between our guide and the young man. Our guide said he was sure that I wouldn't have to hand them in. It became clear that the local Maoist leader had been called for and after a while a man in camouflage fatigues came out of the woods carrying a sub-machine gun. The situation was then resolved very quickly as I handed over my prized binoculars at gunpoint. They asked me to provide them with my address so they could send them on to me. Needless to say I'm still waiting.

On my return from Nepal, I set about replacing my binoculars. I was aware that it was very unlikely that I would find a pair exactly the same as they had been out of production for years. I decided to try eBay and much to my surprise I found a couple of pairs that were the same. I missed the first pair but was determined to win the second which I did. On receipt of them I couldn't believe my eyes – they looked brand new. There wasn't even a mark on the leather case.

I contacted the seller and asked how he had found them. It turned out he had got them from Germany and that the story was that a German man had been given them as a retirement present, put them in a drawer and never used them. I think it was after he died that they came into the possession of the son who obviously sold them on. To say that I was overjoyed would be an understatement. The new pair have since survived another two trips to Nepal!

Des Evans

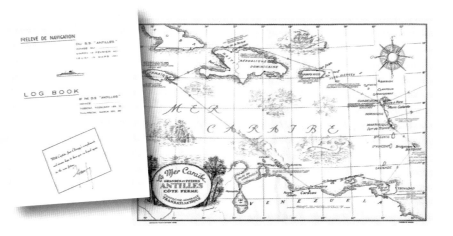

This map shows the month-long voyage around the Caribbean of the cruise ship the SS *Antilles* in 1961. Binoculars are likely to have been packed in the suitcases of many of the wealthy travellers who enjoyed cruising in the 1960s

LANDMARK BINOCULARS:
THE CARL ZEISS JENA 7X50, 8X30 & 10X50

Mass-produced optical excellence

THREE OF THE most successful binoculars in history were produced by the optical giant Zeiss and sold in their hundreds of thousands owing to their impressive optical performance. The Carl Zeiss Jena central focus Binoctem 7x50, Deltrintem 8x30 and Dekarem 10x50 (also available in individual focus Binoctar, Deltrentis and Dekaris versions) are without doubt some of the most enduring binocular designs in history.

These three binoculars found a ready market for both military and civilian use thanks to high standards of production and excellent optical quality. Their magnification range meant that they appealed to a very wide range of users – from sailors at sea to hunters on shore. The 7x50 Binoctar model in particular is thought to have played an especially important role for merchant navies in the first half of the 20th century.

> 'I must admit that I am amazed at the light-gathering power of the binoculars, which makes their use a real, incomparable pleasure even at late dusk or early dawn and in dull weather.'
>
> Dr Hugo Eckner, chairman of the Zeppelin company commenting on the Dekar 10x50 binocular

The 8x30 and 10x50 models offered wide-angle viewing thanks to their Erfle eyepieces. When the 10x50 Dekaris was launched in 1929 its enormous field of view (128m at 1,000m, giving an apparent field of some 73 degrees) must have seemed incredible to users of Zeiss's previous x10 models, which covered only about half of the area of this new glass.

All three models survived the turmoil that was to hit Zeiss during and after World War II, which led to the setting up of two separate companies,

divided by the Iron Curtain (▶ page 20). Shortly afterwards, they reappeared with the benefit of Zeiss's patented T-coating which improved the brightness of the image. While a 15x50 Pentekarem/Pentekar model was also released around this time, representing the first new Zeiss Jena glass to appear after the end of World War II, this did not sell in such large numbers and remains a much scarcer binocular today.

During the 1970s, Zeiss Jena produced cheaper versions of the trio which were given the name 'Jenoptem'. Identical to their Binoctem, Deltrintem and Dekarem cousins, even retailers had difficulty explaining why buyers should pay a premium for the non-Jenoptem versions, which typically cost about 20% more. Contemporary literature only refers to the 'modern production methods' that allowed Zeiss to produce these cut-price binoculars. Some commentators have suggested that this price reduction was possible due to less stringent quality control measures; others that it was simply a desperate attempt by an East German company to gain foreign currency.

There is some evidence that the standards of production tended to decline in the last two decades of Zeiss Jena's existence, with more recent models being less robust and with cruder engineering than those of earlier periods. The latest models did, however, from 1978 come with multicoated lenses which utilized Zeiss's fine 3TM system, providing an even brighter image than was possible previously and improving contrast.

The production of these enduring models by Zeiss Jena ended in 1991 following the fall of the Berlin Wall. However,

MY BINOCULAR STORY

Docter Optics bought many of the binocular assets of Carl Zeiss Jena and continued the production of clones of the Zeiss 8x30, 7x50 and 10x50 models for a few years more.

All three models continue to have a strong following among binocular collectors and users, with their prices on eBay seeing some evidence of rising in recent years. The 10x50 glass in particular is still a very fine candidate for an ideal astronomy glass, with its wide field and large objectives, and its second-hand price compares very favourably with even the best 10x50s to come out of Japan or China today.

TECHNICAL SPECIFICATION

CARL ZEISS JENA 7X50 JENOPTEM/BINOCTEM
Field of view: 7.3° (128 m at 1,000 m)
Apparent field: 51°
Exit pupil diameter: 7.1 mm
Weight: 1010 g

TECHNICAL SPECIFICATION

CARL ZEISS JENA 8X30 JENOPTEM/
DELTRINTEM
Field of view: 8.5° (150 m at 1,000 m)
Apparent field: 68°
Exit pupil diameter: 3.8 mm
Weight: 520 g

TECHNICAL SPECIFICATION

CARL ZEISS JENA 10X50 JENOPTEM/DECAREM
Field of view: 7.3° (128 m at 1,000 m)
Apparent field: 73°
Exit pupil diameter: 5 mm
Weight: 1020 g

Note: the technical data refers to the multicoated versions of the binoculars produced from the 1978 onwards

The binoculars that would not die

TWENTY OR SO years ago I went to Chile on a part business-trip and was horrified to discover in Santiago that my binoculars had gone cross-eyed sometime during the flight – they'd obviously been knocked and were completely out of alignment. They weren't top quality (big and heavy, cheap and cheerful 10x50s by Hilka), and to save carrying such a useless weight, I dumped them in a waste basket outside the cathedral. Later, back in my hotel room I got a call from reception that a man wanted to see me. Going down I met a chap holding my bins who said, 'At last I have found you!', and he gave them back to me saying, 'You left these by the Cathedral'. Touched by his concern and honesty I thanked him and put my hand to my wallet to give him a reward for his troubles. He immediately backed off. 'No, please, I only wanted you to have them back', he said and he went. I've no idea how he found me. I did manage to do some birdwatching, with one eye shut, and returned home to saw the bins in half. They are still in rough service as a couple of monoculars. This means that these inexpensive Hilka binoculars have survived one way or another for nearly 40 years.

John Harrison

A turn of the 20th century advertisement from the USA, encouraging readers to purchase a binocular for use sighting ships

ABOVE LEFT: Residents of Leeds can enjoy spectacular views of the cityscape from this specially-constructed platform on the edge of Holbeck cemetery

ABOVE RIGHT: The author and his wife use binoculars during an excursion with friends at the Yorkshire Sculpture Park. The collection includes internationally important works by such figures as Henry Moore, Barbara Hepworth and Andy Goldsworthy

staggering sum of over 220,000 aircraft movements. Today, not even the most keen-eyed aircraft spotter can keep track of all these comings and goings.

Further south on the outskirts of London, it is sometimes possible to see taxi drivers checking out aircraft through binoculars as they wait for their next fares at Heathrow, the largest airport in the UK. Here, they enjoy views of some of the world's biggest aircraft. Up until 2003, this included the majestic spectacle of Concorde, one of only two supersonic passenger aircraft ever to have operated commercially. On most days you are likely to still see plane spotters with binoculars peering over the major runways at Heathrow and the other principal airports of the UK.

The varied used of binoculars to add enjoyment to leisure time are only bounded by the imagination and it seems that any pastime that requires people to see things closer can be enriched by the use of a binocular. In recent months the author has seen people using binoculars to study flowers and trees in public gardens, on walks in upland countryside and in cities to study architecture. In the city of Leeds, the council has teamed up with voluntary groups to build a superb viewing platform at the edge of Holbeck cemetery,

Binoculars can be used to pick out the architectural details of buildings in major cities. Pictured here is St. Paul's House in Leeds, built in 1878

Binoculars are frequently carried on walks and hikes, such as here in the Lake District National Park

which perches high above the city near the Leeds United football ground. Visitors to the platform, including some local residents using binoculars, enjoy watching the changing cityscape of what has been termed the financial capital of the north.

What a wonderful sight awaits students of architecture in California, USA. Here, celebrated Canadian-born architect Frank Gehry collaborated with Claes Oldenburg and Coosje van Bruggen to insert a giant binocular into his Chiat/Day advertising agency building in Venice, which was erected between 1985 and 1991. The binocular forms both the pedestrian and vehicular entrance to the building as well as incorporating two small conference rooms. The 'eyepieces' of the binoculars even act as skylights.

Finally, those people lucky enough to enjoy a commanding view from their homes can spend hours studying the changing scene with a binocular. This relaxing pastime is often made more comfortable by fixing the binocular to a sturdy base for steady long-range viewing.

A Ross 10x80 binocular provides a commanding view from an apartment that looks out over the still waters of the Hudson River, New York. The owner has designed and fabricated a special mounting device which allows the instrument to move up and down, periscope fashion, to the desired height

'He looks through the exquisite binoculars of Zeiss, (the expensive present from King David), and sees all the wrinkles in the granite, and a pine tree or a village as small as an insect.'   Ossip Mandalstam

7 Choosing, using, repairing

So you've decided you want a binocular? The next thing to consider is what make and model you fancy (there are over 500 to choose from) and where you're going to test it out and buy it. Then comes the sometimes perplexing issue of how you're actually going to use it. The instruction book tells you about the mechanical side of your new purchase but there are curiously few instructions on how to get the best out of your binocular in day to day use. And no-one has told you what to do if your binocular goes out of alignment! This chapter explores the way people choose and then use their binoculars. It considers how binocular buying has changed as the market has developed and describes how the internet is transforming things today. It also considers the repair and servicing of binoculars, highlighting growing concern that this is becoming a dying trade. Among the burning questions addressed in the chapter includes the peculiar matter of where — in these days of paranoia over terrorism, paedophiles and people with 'minority' interests – it is still considered socially acceptable to use a binocular in public.

Maurice Marchant, who helps people to choose their binoculars and then repairs them when things go wrong. Maurice works from his base at CleySpy in Norfolk, the UK's largest optical showroom

AN IMPORTANT PART of the story of the social history of binoculars across the ages concerns the choosing, using and repairing of these specialist mechanical and optical instruments. Soon after the large-scale manufacture of binoculars began in the 1800s, numerous different companies were vying for the attention of customers wealthy enough to be able to afford these luxury items. Many eye-catching advertisements are preserved from over a hundred years ago, illustrating the marketing strategies that early companies used to tempt would-be purchasers to choose their products.

An 1898 advertisement from the German company Goerz, providing a very graphic representation of the value of the new prismatic binoculars. These binoculars were one of a range of innovative models that appeared after the Zeiss patent of 1894 was awarded, in this case featuring objective lenses above the level of the eyepieces to avoid infringing the patent

'That eyes may see better and farther'   BAUSCH & LOMB SLOGAN (1920)

The advent of prism binoculars in the final decade of the 19th century provided marketeers with an important new message to convey in the form of hitherto unseen magnification in such a compact package and impressive fields of view, as several early examples of magazine advertisements show.

Other companies used different strategies to bring them commercial advantage. Zeiss was among the first companies to recognise that celebrities could add considerable kudos to the products coming out of their factories. Norwegian polar explorer Roald Amundsen (1872-1928) is just one of the famous people who lent their name to this celebrated marque.

Effective marketing by binocular manufacturers meant that by the outbreak of World War II families lucky enough to have some spare cash for luxuries were often tempted to acquire a binocular, ready for excursions.

Quality counts

I FIRMLY BELIEVE that because cheap optics proliferated the market here some thirty years ago, enthusiasm for a better product never developed. Let's face it to be a 'chocoholic' one has to have first tasted proper chocolate. I live on top of a hill in suburban Sydney (Australia), with fabulous views from the second storey deck. I will often give our visitors a Tasco binocular to look through and there is a modest interest in the view. I then offer to give them a Leica or Zeiss and boy do things change! It's like wearing reading glasses for the first time. The view comes to life. I then pass around some fine binoculars and even someone who wouldn't buy a pair of binoculars will spend the next twenty minutes swapping instruments.

Michael Kaczor

Companies wishing to attract potential binocular purchasers have in more recent years tried a range of tactics and stunts to keep their brand in the public eye. They include an offer of a guaranteed £50 trade-in allowance on old binoculars by Minox and various sponsorship deals of events and publications from high profile companies such as Swarovski. A less conventional development came in the early 2000s with the offer by Leica to loan out special bright red versions of its Trinovid binoculars for more extensive field testing. This company also developed the idea of a 'passport' for a binocular, which promises to repair malfunction caused by accidental damage within two years of purchasing the instrument.

In common with the marketing of other products, binocular manufacturers frequently stage competitions to garner interest in their brand. Large-scale events provide ideal opportunities for such marketing stunts, and could even reward you a top of the range instrument just for the fun of taking part (◆ see box).

These well-dressed American children also sport a gun and a binocular, sure signs that they came from a wealthy family

Purchasing binoculars

Binocular buyers have for many years been able to draw upon a variety of written material to inform their purchasing decisions. Even before World War II some manufacturers issued comprehensive booklets to help customers navigate their way through the plethora of models available.

More independent information followed some time later in the form of magazine reviews in specialist publications aimed at naturalists, hunters and astronomers. Informative booklets also appeared on both sides of the Atlantic, such as the British Trust for Ornithology's

With Amundsen to the South Pole!

Mr. H. M. Bennett
U. S. Agt., Carl Zeiss

Dear Mr. Bennett:

My most prized possession is my Carl Zeiss Binocular, which is just as good today as when I bought it in 1902. It has been my constant companion on every trip for the past 22 years, including my trip to the South Pole. It has withstood every known climatic condition and very severe use. I do not hesitate to recommend Zeiss Binoculars most highly.

The model used by Capt. Amundsen and 20 other models of 3 to 18 power are shown in our complete catalogue. Write for a copy.

Zeiss Binoculars are sold by leading opticians, camera and sporting goods dealers everywhere. Write for our complete catalogue.

HAROLD M. BENNETT, U. S. AGENT, 155 WEST 23rd ST., NEW YORK
Distributing Agents for Canada: The Hughes Owens Co., Ltd., Montreal, Toronto, Winnipeg, Ottawa

CARL ZEISS Prism Binoculars

ABOVE: This image of a family excursion in Washington, D.C. in March 1938 shows that binocular use on outings was an established practice among some American families before the outbreak of World War II

LEFT: Celebrity sponsorship of optics cannot get much bigger than the first person to have reached the South Pole. Amundsen was a major figure during the heroic age of Antarctic exploration

INSET: Binocular buyers visiting overseas destinations could sometimes benefit from generous discounts when on holiday, as this early business postcard from Gibraltar shows

Binoculars, Telescopes & Cameras for the Birdwatcher, published in 1972. This contained helpful guidance on choosing and using binoculars, and compared the range of products available. Optical survey information showing who was using what came in the guise of an occasional series of articles published from 1978 onwards, with the rubber stamp of quality of *British Birds* – one of the UK's longest established nature periodicals. This allowed users to see which models were deemed most suitable for their hobby by fellow discerning users. A few general books on the topic of choosing and using binoculars also appeared, with the publications by Paul (1981) and Seyfried (1995) being especially helpful.

Booklets were issued on both sides of the Atlantic to help customers make better binocular choices. Here, publications by Bausch & Lomb (1935) and Denhill (1956) are pictured

The era of the internet has provided some wonderful new resources to those considering purchasing a new binocular. High quality sites with detailed comparative reviews of a range of models have appeared – probably the most comprehensive yet published. Such sites have also been a major boon to binocular collectors and enthusiasts. The most frequently book-marked are probably the US site Better View Desired (www.betterviewdesired.com) and the superb reviews of German physics professor and optical expert Holger Merlitz (www.holgermerlitz.de).

'To look at things in poor light, when the pupils of your eyes expand from their normal 3 mm diameter to about 7 mm, you will want binoculars that pass as much light as possible to them.'

WHICH? MAGAZINE

MY BINOCULAR STORY

Spot the warbler!

BETTY NEEDHAM, FROM Derbyshire, took part in a 'spot the warbler' competition organised by Zeiss at the 1992 British Birdfair, never thinking that she would be the winner of the 8x20B binoculars offered as first prize.

Betty started birdwatching in 1974 when she joined the RSPB nationally and also linked up with the local Coventry branch. Despite being a 'townie', she had always had an interest in natural history from the days of Romany on the wireless to evacuation in 1941 to the Isle of Man.

The competition involved

the placing of a pin in a picture of some reeds, much like the familiar 'spot the ball' football competitions. Yet Betty's pin

was spot on and she was thrilled to receive a letter from Zeiss a week or so later to say she was the winner!

Up until that point Betty had been a Zeiss user, but her choice had been the much larger and heavier East German 10x50 Jenoptem model. The compact model from the west came as something of a revelation, and has been used by Betty ever since. She especially enjoys using it on walks, and has found it useful for spotting the location of the footpath markers that show she is on the correct route.

Buyers today are blessed – or should that be burdened – with so many choices as to where to acquire their binoculars. High street stores, specialist shops, internet sites, eBay, flea markets, militaria events and car boot sales all offer pros and cons to the buyer. Perhaps the worst option, as confirmed by numerous unhappy customers, is to head to a shop selling consumer goods such as electrical or camping equipment – of which there are numerous chains in the UK and North America. These shops tend to have a poor selection of models, inadequate indoor testing facilities and staff who know little about optics. The author was amazed to find out that even staff working in a specialist chain of camera stores in the UK that also stocks binoculars are not trained in the basics of optics.

Bird conservation organisations saw a growth in membership during the post war years, leading to the issuing of special information leaflets on such matters as selecting and caring for binoculars. These 21st century examples are the latest versions to have come off the presses

'There can be no doubt that the best binoculars are amongst the most expensive, although this is not to say that the most expensive binoculars are certainly the best. There are not many of us, however, who can put our hands in our pockets and pull out the odd £70 for a pair of new Zeiss binoculars just when we feel like it; and consequently we have to look at the range of binoculars offered and try and work out what is best value for the money we have begged, borrowed or saved.'   PETER CONDER (1963)

A much better option, and a growing trend in many countries, is to spend a few hours at a specialist optical shop. Though small in number, there are some excellent – usually independently-owned – stores whose owners have a wealth of experience and a real passion for binoculars. Depending on your specific area of interest there are shops showcasing binoculars for astronomy, birdwatching or hunting.

Binocular buyers are sometimes surprised to hear that the most experienced sellers do not recommend a particular model as the 'best' for their intended use. This is because the weight, balance and comfort of using any instrument is as important as the optical quality; there is no use purchasing an instrument with superb quality lenses if it is too heavy or the eyepieces simply do not suit the user's facial anatomy. Furthermore, although image brightness and resolution can be determined through objective and highly-controlled tests in the workshop, people do not see exactly the same picture when looking through a binocular. For example, colour cast perception and the user's susceptibility to colour fringing around the edge of brightly-lit objects varies from person to person. This is why it is so important to test the widest range of models in the chosen price bracket before making a final decision. And because lighting conditions can affect a binocular's performance too, it is vital to try them out under a variety of skies.

'The design of every binocular is a matter of compromise, and the designer must decide which particular advantage he is going to stress; for he can only stress one value at the expense of others.'

HOW TO CHOOSE A BINOCULAR, PUBLISHED BY J.A.DAVIS & SON LTD (1955)

Comparative articles on binoculars published in specialist magazines provide invaluable information for those considering new purchases

Many binocular buyers understandably assume that *every* example of a model from a particular manufacturer has identical optical performance, whereas in fact individual variation is quite common. It seems that some binoculars have been put together using especially fine batches of glass, or their lenses are more carefully coated than others, despite identical external appearances. The tight mechanical tolerances of binoculars also means that even tiny differences in production standards can affect optical quality or functionality. For these reasons, buyers are often recommended to look through the actual binocular they are taking away with them, rather than receive a boxed, unopened example from the shop storeroom. Some binocular enthusiasts refer to the best-performing binoculars from a particular batch as 'cherries' and these can outperform models by other manufacturers that are usually thought to be of superior optical quality.

Some buyers take the rather uncharitable decision to try out a wide range of brands in a specialist shop and then go online to find the best deals. While this might seem to have obvious benefits, there are many so-called 'grey imports' on the market – binoculars imported from overseas whose warranty may not be valid in the country of purchase. The internet is also the place where disreputable dealers can hide behind professional-looking websites. Another option is the internet auction site eBay, which is particularly popular with those seeking scarcer used binoculars, and is discussed in the next chapter. The successful online shop Microglobe owes its success partly to the highly competitive prices it places on binoculars, which are often available for substantially less than elsewhere. The enterprising owners of this London-based outfit now sell such quantities of binoculars that they can negotiate attractive discounts from big name manufacturers such as Canon.

'Although Denhill are the best binoculars for everyday use, if more specialised German binoculars are required, be sure to buy a pair with a genuine reputable German name, such as Zeiss, Voigtländer or Wohler for instance. Some dealers use German names to sell binoculars which are cheap and inferior in pattern and design.'

How to Choose a Binocular, published by J.A.Davis & Son Ltd (1955)

The cost of new binoculars varies enormously. At the bottom end of the market, cheap models can be picked up – even from supermarkets or gift shops – for as little as £10, but the top price models sold by specialist dealers are now pushing £1,500. Such a huge variation in price is strangely not matched by a similarly wide performance range in binoculars. While those models costing less than £25 are usually quite poor compared to those priced over £100, many are still perfectly useable. In the £100 to £300 price bracket many excellent binoculars can be found whose optical performance laypeople might find hard to distinguish from the high-end models. And once you start paying over £400 you may

THE CLEYSPY STORY

NORFOLK'S CLEYSPY IS certainly the largest binocular shop in the UK and may even be the biggest in Europe. Started from humble beginnings in 2001, this fiercely independent playground for the binocular enthusiast now stocks the widest range of binoculars one could ever hope to see assembled in one place.

The business was started through a partnership between businessmen Paul Marriot and John Hullah, and birdwatcher and optics expert Steve Harris. While the business nous and confidence of Marriot and Hullah were significant in the early days of the company, it was Harris's wealth of knowledge of binoculars and telescopes, coupled with a real charm in putting this across to customers, that brought buyers back to CleySpy. Though Hullah left the business in 2004, further expansion followed and new staff joined the team as CleySpy saw its reputation as a leading optical showroom grow. Additional staff members joining the team were selected for their enthusiasm for optics and skill in helping customers make appropriate choices.

Location, location

CleySpy's main shop is located in the pretty village of Glandford, which hides itself away from the main coast road across North Norfolk in the valley of the river Glaven. Visitors are alerted to the presence of the shop by a distinctive, monolith-like giant binocular, painted bright yellow and situated on a stand adjacent to the road. This is a deliberate nod to the primitive tradesmen's signs of the Middle Ages. The shop is situated in a former carrot-washing barn which is at least 150 years' old and has been named the Sir Alfred Jodrell Barn after a former owner of the Bayfield Estate, who built much of the village. CleySpy commands impressive views over the surrounding countryside,

Paul Marriot, owner of CleySpey

THE CLEYSPY STORY *Continued*

which makes it ideal for binocular testing. It takes its name from a clever play on words linked to the famous bird reserve just east of the nearby village of Cley next the Sea. Clever that is, if you pronounce Cley as 'Cly', which does annoy some locals would prefer it pronounced 'Clay'!

One of the principal factors that has contributed to the success of the business is its strategic location a few miles from the Norfolk coast. The fact that people called in to a nearby shell museum asking where they could buy binoculars showed that there was a niche to be filled by an enterprising team. The area attracts tens of thousands of birdwatchers every year, who come in search of the spectacular goose and wading bird concentrations on this internationally important coastline. They are also attracted to the wind-blown rarities that crop up from time to time. The region is also popular with boat owners, holiday makers and others who enjoy the landscape and wide open skies of this wild part of England. All these people are also attracted to optics, and CleySpy provides the ideal location where they can equip themselves with binoculars to enrich their passions. In the words of Steve Harris, 'Binoculars are an invaluable tool in North Norfolk.'

Secrets of success

As with any successful business, hard work is a vital ingredient in the story. During the early years the team worked seven days a week, even though Steve had actually taken 'early retirement' from his role as conservation officer for Norfolk County Council.

Another key member of the CleySpy team is optical technician Maurice Marchant. As well as servicing and repairing instruments, Maurice brings with him decades of knowledge about the buying and selling of optics,

which is now put to good effect when he helps out with sales. Maurice has worked on some incredible optical instruments during his long career as an optical repairman. Chief among these was the huge German ex-military binocular which naturalist Peter Scott bought after the war for use at his fledgling Slimbridge wildfowl reserve on the Severn Estuary.

An important part of the ethos at CleySpy is that the team would rather not make a sale to a customer, than send them away with them something inappropriate. This attitude, together with complete independence, helps customers make the best choices for their chosen needs rather than leave the shop with a more lucrative 'own brand'.

An innovative development has seen CleySpy team up with marketing professionals to launch

an advert which can be heard on North Norfolk radio. It may well be the only radio advert for binoculars in the UK. Observant members of the public are also invited to look out for CleySpy stickers in the windows of the radio station's cars, being rewarded with a free binocular if they are the first to report it to the shop.

For several years the CleySpy complex was also home to the UK's only binocular museum, the brainchild of Harris, and containing all sorts of historically interesting instruments. Among them were several scarce models that were not on display at museums overseas. While this facility has unfortunately now had to give way to an outdoor clothing display due to economic pressures, there are hopes that a new optics museum

might be resurrected at some point in the future.

Another development has been the establishment of a farm walk and nearby birdwatching hide in collaboration with the Combe family, present owners of the Bayfield Estate. This has brought additional people to the area, some of whom now take binoculars into the hide for more extended testing sessions.

A view to the future

As the business has evolved so the ownership balance has changed. Although Harris now runs a wildlife art gallery with his wife in an adjacent barn – fulfilling a lifelong dream – he continues to be a key adviser to CleySpy as well as being the weekend manager in the shop.

This is helping the business to understand new trends in optics buying, as well as keeping abreast of technological advances by the major manufacturers.

Seven years after the company was set up the core values of CleySpy are apparent to all who visit this optical showroom – values that are continuing to pay dividends. In 2007 the company won the contract to run a new optics shop at the Norfolk Wildlife Trust's flagship reserve at Cley Marshes. This new facility – a much cosier version than the headquarters in Glandford – is situated in a thatched visitor centre overlooking the reed-dotted lagoons of Cley and the North Sea beyond. It is fitting that CleySpy finally seems to have come home.

▶ *www.cleyspy.co.uk*

This Zeiss
advertisement
from 10 December
1910 reminds
readers that
binoculars make
ideal presents

need to test binoculars in really hostile conditions to see the benefits of spending more. This price-performance relationship leads many binocular salespeople to recommend that while it is generally true that the more you pay the better your binocular will be, above about £400 improvements in performance can be marginal. Those people paying the top prices for models made by Leica, Nikon, Swarovski and Zeiss certainly pay a premium for the name, and perhaps are also tempted by the excellent after-sales service that the big names offer.

Binoculars make ideal presents, as they can last a lifetime and there are so many price entry points. It is not uncommon to find binoculars imprinted with dedications from family, friends or work colleagues. Occasionally, examples come on the market that have been given to senior employees of the major binocular manufacturers, for example to thank them for winning a major contract, or on retirement. Some binoculars are passed – in moving circumstances – on to others as part of the Will and Testament of the previous user (◆ see box).

Perhaps the most helpful piece of guidance that the author has heard in relation to choosing and purchasing binoculars is that any final purchase is likely to be a *compromise* of one kind or another. It is a mistake to think in terms of a 'perfect' binocular for all conditions, even within a narrow field of interest such as birdwatching or astronomy. There always seems to be at least one minor feature of a binocular that the user would like to change, hence buying decisions should centre around which compromises buyers are prepared to accept, while keeping the binocular within an acceptable price range.

'When choosing look at the smallest possible detail – perhaps a brick or a notice at least 100 yards away and try each pair of binoculars in turn, trying to spot the smallest detail you can. I recently did this with a pair of medium-priced, but well-advertised binoculars and some very low-priced Japanese binoculars. As I result I bought the Japanese binoculars which were three times less expensive than the "popular" brand. I am now convinced I had excellent value for money.'
PETER CONDER

A binocular glass has been awarded by the President of the United States to Captain Thomas Evans, master of the London steamer North Cambria, for rescuing the crew of an American schooner last November

THE TIMES NEWSPAPER, 18 JUNE 1917

In January 2008 a Carl Zeiss Jena 6x30 Silvarem binocular (serial no. 233264; c.1911) appeared on eBay with the following inscription:

TO WM HALL CALVERT ESQ. M.D.
FROM GRATEFUL PATIENTS AND
ATTACHED FRIENDS. MELROSE
13TH OCT 1911

Buyers are also encouraged to consider that, rather like a new pair of shoes, it often takes some time to get used to a new binocular – a period of acclimatisation can usually be expected. This is why it is important not to expect the viewing to be 'just right' the first time you try out a new binocular; it is likely that your eyes and face will have become accustomed to your current model over the years.

Myths and stereotypes

During the author's teenage years one of his friends was a plane spotter and he a birdwatcher. As soon as he got his first full size binocular – a Carl Zeiss Jena 10x50 Jenoptem – he proudly showed it to his friend. 'They're rubbish!' his friend proclaimed, much to the author's annoyance, 'Mine are 20x50, they're much better.'

This myth – that higher power in binoculars must be better – still exists to this day. While it does hold a certain kind of logic (distant objects must be easier to see if they appear even closer) it ignores the practicalities of binocular use: that it is virtually impossible to hold steady binoculars over x10 magnification due to hand shake. It also defies one of the key principles of optical design – that

MY BINOCULAR STORY

He has letters after his name
DENNIS BROWN, from Maryport in Cumbria, had been recovering from some personal difficulties when fellow Cumbrian Jim Walsh introduced him to the world of birds. Jim was a local expert on birds and keen to share his knowledge with others.

Over the course of several years Jim took Dennis to a variety of sites in Cumbria in search of birds. The nature reserve at Campfield Marsh was a real favourite and it was here that Dennis learnt to identify some of the trickier species. None of this would have been possible without Jim's immense knowledge and patience – and the occasional look through his state-of-the-art Swarovski 10x42 EL binocular.

Dennis soon discovered that spending time outdoors in the company of Jim helped to heal mental and physical wounds. He was inspired to help as a volunteer at several local sites, even becoming part of the nest protection team for the only pair of nesting ospreys in the Cumbrian Lake District.

Tragically, a few years later Jim was diagnosed with lung cancer and died aged 71 soon afterwards. Later that year his widow telephoned Dennis, saying she had something for him. On arriving at the house, Dennis was overwhelmed when she handed him Jim's Swarovski binocular, which had been left to Dennis in his will.

Birdwatching continues to be Dennis's main passion, helping to ease the bad memories of the past and ready him for the challenges of the future. Jim's binocular is always by his side, helping Dennis to enjoy the majesty of the natural world. One of his recent projects was to install tree sparrow nesting boxes at a farm site – helping this now scarce bird maintain its foothold in Cumbria. He describes birds as the best thing that ever happened to him.

But it is Jim, above all, that Dennis speaks of most fondly and whom he misses deeply on those birdwatching trips. When asked to sum up his friend Dennis puts it so simply, 'He has letters after his name does Jim – BME: Best Man Ever.'

high magnification will make objects appear very dim unless a correspondingly larger objective lens is used. Despite this, it is still common to see advertised today binoculars – often zoom models – with prestigious magnifications, often also with tiny objective lenses which make them essentially useless to the naïve people who purchase them.

Many people also still mistakenly think that the larger the objective size of a binocular, the wider the field of view must be. This is quickly dispelled by comparing, for example, wide-angle models such as the Russian 6x24 made by Komz, with more conventional 6x30 binoculars which cover only about half the area of the 'smaller' glass. Another issue that can cause confusion if you are not used to using binoculars is the question of what you actually see when you look through them. When depicted on film and in print people using binoculars are usually shown to be studying a figure of eight view of the world, as if looking through two linked eye holes in a mask (➤ page 179). In fact, when correctly adjusted for the distance between the user's eyes, binoculars give a perfectly circular view. It is only when they are out of alignment – or used at minimum close focussing distance – that they show anything approaching that which we often see depicted and this makes them impossible to use due to eyestrain!

'In selecting binoculars or telescopes do not yield to the common urge to get the highest possible magnifying power for the investment you plan to make. That is like buying an automobile solely on the basis of the maximum speed which the dealer claims it can attain.'　　　　　　　　　　　　　　ERNEST CHERRINGTON

Contrary to some people's belief conventional binoculars cannot *enhance* the image of a distant object by making it brighter or sharper than the naked eye can see. However, some high quality binoculars – especially those with large diameter objective lenses or with the latest high quality optical coatings – can give the impression of brightening the picture during poor light. This seems to be an optical illusion caused by your eyes and brain concentrating on a narrow field of view compared with what your naked eye would normally see.

The recent appearance of cheap 'ruby coated' binoculars from China can be seen as no more than a marketing trick, as this does not appear to convey any optical advantage. In fact, it can result in a rather blue tint to the image due to the elimination of some light rays from the red part of the spectrum from the picture. The marketeers behind these binoculars are perhaps trying to suggest that their reddish lens tint might have something to do with infra-red night vision binoculars.

A final myth was driven by some of the marketing efforts that accompanied the appearance of roof prism binoculars, which became the object of desire for many purchasers, especially after Leitz launched its Trinovid range in 1963. Many laypeople to this day mistakenly believe that roof prism binoculars are inherently better than Porros – while the reverse is true, certainly in terms of optical quality.

Let's accessorise

Binocular users have long found that a few choice accessories can improve the enjoyment and longevity of binoculars. Although the recent commercial 'accessorising' of binoculars has seen a range of new products emerge onto the market, there were many early improvisers. In his 1953 book *Watching Birds* James Fisher writes: *'My father used a chamois-leather bag which slipped over the glasses and tied in a bow at the top.'*

The use of coloured filters to improve viewing has been discussed in the chapter on the military use of binoculars. However, these were not the only binocular accessories to have found a use in times of conflict. Eyepiece covers – sometimes called rainguards – made of leather, Bakelite, rubber or plastic were a common feature of early military binoculars, some even dating back to World War I. As well as helping to keep rain and sea spray off the exposed glass surfaces, these devices prevent dust and other detritus from accumulating in the sunken eyepiece cavities. Their effectiveness meant that they were also appreciated by civilian binocular users, and during the late 20th century started to become standard issue with most new binoculars. At the time of writing the rainguards of premium manufacturers are also available for sale separately and alone can cost as much as a cheap compact binocular!

Rainguards are now commonly issued with binoculars, helping users to keep lenses free of water and debris

Binoculars are usually supplied with a neck strap of varying quality, traditionally made of leather. There has been a trend in more recent years for such straps to be made thicker and more effective at bearing weight, sometimes through the use of rubber or neoprene. While some users choose not to attach the strap – for example those on the bridge of ships where it may be a hindrance – others use a special harness system that distributes the weight of the binocular on the user's shoulders rather than the neck. This also has the benefit of preventing the binocular from swinging about on a person's chest. The author discovered the benefits of such harnesses only recently, but would now never go back to the traditional arrangement. Some users choose to keep their binocular (usually a compact model) in its case and attach that to their belt, taking advantage of any loop present on the case. The author saw this approach used successfully by an American tourist during a walking safari in Zimbabwe. The binocular was handy for use but did not swing around as she hiked through challenging terrain with a backpack.

People have probably tried to take photographs through their binoculars almost as long as cameras have been in existence, since one half of a binocular has much in common with a high power camera lens. Books such as Cooper's *Photography Through Monoculars, Binoculars and Telescopes* (published in 1965) helped people to get the most from this hobby and in the last decade or so the rise of high quality digital cameras has taken binocular photography to a new level. Recognising the potential of the binocular to produce stunning close-ups of wildlife, the Austrian manufacturer Swarovski recently began to issue a special 'snapshot' digital adapter for their roof prism binoculars, thereby making the process of binocular photography a little easier.

Cases

The author Ernest Hemmingway was known for being a frequent user of binoculars, and once described how he kept them in a woolly sock, complete with a cleaning cloth, when they were not in use. He was surely aware that the traditional material for the binocular case is leather made from cow hide, often reinforced by wood, metal or other inflexible materials. For the first few decades of binocular manufacture, the quality of workmanship evident in cases matched that of the binoculars themselves. This is supported by the survival of hundred-year-old binocular cases of high quality, which still serve their purpose well.

Leather cases have a few drawbacks, however, for both manufacturers and users. First, they are quite expensive to produce; indeed many advertisements from before World War II quoted the price of the case separately, allowing users to decide if they could afford one. Second, the moisture contained in the leather can enter the binocular if it is kept for long periods in its case, leading to the accumulation of a thin film of haze on the glass surfaces with a corresponding loss of optical performance (this is why collectors tend to keep their binoculars out of their cases). Third, leather is quite durable and looks magnificent polished but is not that good at absorbing shocks. The author has dropped binoculars *inside* their leather cases and found them to be out of alignment.

The advent of cheap synthetic fabrics after World War II, including many which are ideal for padding, might be presumed to have signalled a new era in high quality binocular case design. Unfortunately, manufacturers generally did not cover themselves in glory in this respect during those decades. Despite being precision optical and mechanical instruments, many binocular makers carried on supplying leather or imitation leather cases, or instead provided thin, flimsy or otherwise inadequate cases which simply did not serve their intended purpose of protecting the binocular from damage.

A high quality binocular case by US manufacturer Tamrac, one of the few companies to make a case specifically for binoculars

It seems that it is only in the last decade that careful thought has finally been given to designing durable binocular cases with users in mind. It is, therefore, becoming more and more common – even in medium- or low-end brands – to find binocular cases that are waterproof, durable and actually withstand the daily wear and tear that many users inflict on them. Unfortunately, until recently the high-end manufacturers continued the practice of charging extra for a proper binocular case. One would have hoped that paying £1,000 for a binocular would secure you a high quality case too, but users needed to dig deeper into their pockets to purchase – at a premium price – a case for their pride and joy.

There are still curious anomalies in binocular case design. The author recently bought a used Miranda 8x30 of poor optical quality for a few pounds simply because it had one of the finest adjustable padded cases he had ever seen, into which a wide variety of other models fit snugly. While the case is in daily use, the binocular quickly found its way to the charity shop.

Given the stated dearth of high quality cases, it is rather surprising that more companies have not exploited this gap in the market by producing purpose-made binocular cases, much like those made for cameras. Many modern binocular users actually improvise by using cases designed first and foremost for some other device. The US company Tamrac seems virtually alone as a pioneer in this area, producing one of the only cases designed specifically for binoculars which can comfortably fit

MY BINOCULAR STORY

What do those markings mean?

I WAS LEADING an adult education class to a local nature reserve a few years ago. Normally the success of such a trip is gauged by the number of birds the students see but not for a particular lady. She asked me what the function was of the markings around the right-hand eyepiece. I replied that they were for focussing the eyepiece to allow for the difference in her two eyes. She looked rather blank so I showed her how to set up the binoculars properly. She was, to say the least, over the moon, exclaiming that she could now see a clear picture for the first time. She called her husband over and showed him too. She said it was worth coming for that alone. How much you take for granted!

Dave Emley

MY BINOCULAR STORY

The value of wide-field binoculars

IN THE MILITARY, as a Demonstration Platoon Commander, I was tasked with ordering fire the moment the advancing officer cadets passed a certain hedge line. Since I had the use of a 6x30 binocular I decided to make quite sure not to miss the moment and I trained my binocular, rested on the edge of my trench, on the wide gap in the hedge through which some of the advancing platoons were sure to pass. I waited and waited. Then over the wireless, 'Mr Gregory, what the hell are you up to? Open Fire!' My Commanding Officer! I concurred, seeing for the first time, to my horror, advancing soldiers in the field in front of me, instead of two fields away.

Of course the advancing troops had not passed through the wide gap of which I had been so sure. Even the unaided eye would have been a surer way of detecting the advance, but a wider field binocular with constant panning would have also served.

In Zimbabwe, when trying to stalk up on a herd of buffalo to secure photographs, I carried a 6x30 Swarovski, with field the normal 150 at 1,000, with rubber-armouring added by myself, using the inner tube of a bicycle tyre. This armouring excited considerable interest from the Customs on my return to the UK. I like to think they appreciated the quality of my workmanship, and were admiring it, but I fear they might have felt I was trying to conceal something tucked inside!

This Swarovski was unsurpassed in sharpness for a 6x30. I had also a more easily pocketable Russian Foton 5x25 with a wide field of some 212 m at 1,000 m. Now the area of the field covered by the Foton is almost exactly double that of the Swarovski. This wide field allowed me to glimpse, at the field edge, an enormous elephant feeding from the trees, only 50 yards from me! I was searching, as I advanced, for any members of the buffalo herd. Had I been using the 6x30 for this scanning I think I would not have glimpsed the elephant, since it was right at the edge of the field of view of the wide-angle binocular.

The Sard 6x42 has the same wide-angle as the Foton, but, at 3.75 pounds (1.7 kg) in weight it

a wide range of makes and models. Their padded and waterproof case is a joy once discovered, though it can be strangely difficult to track one down. It certainly lives up to the company's slogan 'No-one carries it off better'!

How to use them

Given that the basic operation of a binocular might seem rather obvious, it is often surprising to learn that users – especially of centre focus models – have not set them up properly for their own eyes. Despite most instruction booklets giving details of how to adjust the dioptre setting and focus wheel to achieve sharp images, making the necessary adjustments seems to be beyond many users. Unfortunately, many sellers do not provide an adequate demonstration before purchases are made, which means that the binocular may never be set properly for a user's eyes. This can lead to eyestrain and a feeling that users 'just can't get on with binoculars'.

The myth that higher magnification must be better was touched upon earlier. This leads on to the topic of 'apparent magnification', which is an important

would prove quite a formidable burden in the heat as it would be in addition to the camera with its 400mm lens. When I got close to the buffalo I decided to climb a low rocky cliff, hoping that this might prove some sort of an obstacle for any aggressive buffalo. Peering over the top I espied a good bull, close enough for its head and neck to 'fill the frame' in the viewfinder. I had taken about four pictures when there came a loud 'humf' from one of the buffalo: the herd dashed off. I decided to pace out the distance at which I had taken the photographs and was halfway through my pacing, when I glanced to the right side to see a huge buffalo bull, only 10-15 yards from me! I was at his mercy should he have decided to charge. Luckily,

as I lost any thought of completing my pacing and went into reverse, he did nothing. My best chance of detecting him would have been to use a wide-angle binocular, such as the Foton, before advancing. It would not guarantee detection, but, combined with a period of observation with the naked eye it would be the best strategy if the circumstances recur.

It is movement that most surely and most often reveals the presence of animals. This movement shows itself almost equally well at the edge of a wide-field binocular field, although the definition may be imperfect, compared with the sharpest central point. It still catches the attention. This probably explains the design specification of the Zeiss and

Leitz 8x60 with field of 150-160 at 1,000, the 6x42 Sard with 212 at 1,000, the Bausch & Lomb Widefield 7x50 with 175 at 1,000, the Zeiss 8x40 Deltar, 198 at 1,000, and the Huet 8x40 with 188 at 1,000. All these were designed for naval use or for the detection of aircraft, and, in most cases, are heavier than the average Sunday afternoon stroller would select as a convenient companion. Yet the same wide field can be obtained with a 5x25 without the bulk and weight penalty. For close-range use, or for searching ground, there is an awful lot in favour of the near constant focus of these low-power glasses.

Robert Gregory
(Robert is a binocular enthusiast and author, and a former teacher at Eton College)

consideration when using binoculars. The hand-shake that sometimes results from using a binocular of x10 power can render useless its higher magnification, meaning that it cannot resolve detail any better than a binocular of x8 or even x7 magnification – unless it is held steady by artificial means. This has led to many people choosing lower power binoculars for everyday use. Many users also chose wide-angle binoculars, as these give them an advantage in seeing more of the sports field or nature reserve (➧ see box).

The tripod mounting of binoculars is a pleasure that has curiously not been experienced by most users. They are perhaps ignorant of the fact that due to hand shake they are not able to enjoy the optimum performance of binoculars in most situations – even those of lower power. Few people realise that many full size binoculars come with an in-built thread, situated at the objective end of the bending bar, which can be used to attach them to a tripod with a suitable adapter. Models that do not incorporate such a feature can usually be fixed to a tripod using another type of mounting mechanism. Some enterprising manufacturers have even produced

Almost all binoculars come with an instruction manual for users. These 1950s and 1970s examples from Carl Zeiss Jena and Swift both fold into small packages but are unusually comprehensive

universal wrap-around mounts that allow a wide range of models to be attached to a tripod (▶ page 77). Using such equipment, many people are surprised at the jump in optical quality and relaxed viewing that is made possible.

The growth in interest of bird and mammal observation at sea, on so-called pelagic trips, has led to the more widespread use of monopods for binocular use by nature enthusiasts. With the binocular firmly attached to the monopod, steady observation of subjects over or on the sea surface is possible, despite the movement of the ship, yet the facility is still maintained to scan swiftly across the area being viewed. Similar devices made of wood are sometimes referred to as 'Finn sticks' following their use by pioneering Scandinavian observers. Originally, they would have been fashioned from sticks with the binocular perched on top, or perhaps with a simple leather strap to attach to it to the sturdy base.

The various users of binoculars have developed specific tactics or techniques for maximising their professional interest or hobby. They show that the advanced use of optics requires a suite of practical skills that can be practised and developed. Birdwatchers in particular have developed an impressive range of strategies for finding and identifying their quarry. For example, they are to be found scanning hedges, lake margins and telegraph wires for birds as frequently as they are actually watching them.

Some people make unconventional choices when it comes to using binoculars. For example, the author knows a retired lady who prefers to use a small, lightweight opera glass when watching birds in her garden and when out on

MY BINOCULAR STORY

The south of France

DURING MY EARLY years as a teenage birdwatcher I was excited to be offered the chance to travel to the south of France on a school exchange visit. Although the main aim of the trip was meant to be to improve my knowledge of the French language and culture, birds were the principal thing on my mind – especially the exotic looking species, the bee-eaters, hoopoes and rollers – for which the Mediterranean coast is famous.

On a hot sunny day (in fact the sun shone every day of my stay), we headed to a nearby beach as my friends and pen-friend were more interested in swimming and sunbathing than birdwatching. As I always did I took along my binoculars and decided to take a stroll along the beach towards some dunes where I hoped I might find some wildlife.

I was a few hundred yards into my trek when my pen-friend unexpectedly rushed up to me. While I could not understand the nuances of what he was saying I could see the notice he was pointing at on the beach behind me, which I had missed as I gazed at a honey buzzard circling inland. The notice was in French but I understood perfectly the gist of what it meant – 'No unauthorised persons…this is a private nudist beach'.

As we turned swiftly around and jogged back to the rest of the group in fits of laughter, I resisted the temptation to sneak at look through my binoculars at the bronzed beauties baring their naked bodies to the Mediterranean sun. I have to admit it was difficult – as a teenage boy feathered birds were not the only kind on my mind!

BB

walks. She uses a lower power Edwardian glass, which is quick and easy to use and can be slipped in her pocket or handbag. For use from her house, she describes them as perfect for studying birds visiting her garden. Her preference for an opera glass should not necessarily be seen as giving her a disadvantage. In fact the simplicity of opera glasses, with few internal glass surfaces compared to prismatic binoculars (each of which reflects back some light),

gives them excellent light gathering powers. The author has used World War I x6 Galilean binoculars to good effect in poor light when uncoated prismatic binoculars from the same decade were struggling to transmit enough light for viewing. The landmark publication in 1888 of *Astronomy with an Opera Glass* was the catalyst for a growth in interest in the night sky in the USA, demonstrating the usability of Galilean instruments.

This early Barr & Stroud cleaning instruction helped pre-war binocular users to gain maximum benefit from their purchase. Note the reference to the lack of optical coatings, which were added to British civilian binoculars only after World War II

In order to enjoy the full optical performance of binoculars it is important to keep the external lenses clean. Given the fairly obvious link between detritus and dust on the lenses and the clarity of vision, it is surprising how many people seem to neglect the cleaning of their binoculars. It is not uncommon to find second-hand instruments which have obviously not been cleaned for decades. The step change in performance that is possible with a little careful cleaning is one of the joys of restoring a neglected binocular. Most binoculars are now issued with a cleaning cloth made of special material that does not scratch the coating. The best are the lint-free microfibre cloths which do not leave tiny particles of fluff on the lenses. Instruction booklets guide users in the cleaning of their binoculars, explaining the need to remove potentially damaging grit particles before wiping the lens surfaces.

There is, however, a careful balance to be struck between keeping the lens surfaces of a binocular free of dirt and *overcleaning* them. This is a lesson that the author learnt the hard way during his teenage years, with over-zealous cleaning of his Carl Zeiss Jenoptem 10x50 leading to the partial stripping of the lens coatings. While eye-lash oil and grease can reduce the optical performance of binoculars, a few specks of dust are not going to be visible when the instrument is used and binocular experts suggest that these are better ignored. Compared to the external treatment of lens surfaces to optimise performance, the *internal* cleaning of binoculars is a highly-specialised task that owners are recommended not to attempt themselves.

Where to use them

One morning the author was scanning with his binocular over the river near his house when he heard someone call out from a passing car – 'Get a life!' they yelled. Clearly this person must have already had a bad day, but this incident made him think about where it is 'socially acceptable' to use binoculars in the 21st century. Where can one still use binoculars and blend seamlessly into the surroundings, without giving rise to rude comments from passers-by?

MY BINOCULAR STORY

Splashing out on some new binoculars

IT WAS A warm and sunny day in June when I decided to test out my new expensive Zeiss 10x40B binoculars, purchased the previous day. My friend, Dorothy, and I went to a local area with woods and fields through which a small river ran, which was usually a good place to see many different species of birds.

The banks of the river had been cut back by the council to form vertical cliffs three feet in height. The water was only about six inches deep, clear when it ran over stones but muddy in parts.

As Dorothy and I walked along in single file on top of the bank we were chatting, as one does, and at one point I turned round to answer her when my foot found a rabbit hole causing me to trip and fall flat on my face into the water! My thoughts were of my bins which were of course round my neck, and so I clasped them to my chest as I fell into the water.

Luckily, I had chosen a clear stony part of the river to splash into. I was wet from head to toe and the stones had grazed my bare arms and legs. Dorothy just stood on the bank laughing, not only at the sight of me but because I could not climb the recently cut banks, thus forcing me to walk along the river until I could find somewhere to climb out.

The sun dried me out but when we again met other friends we had seen before the incident, they too burst out laughing with little sympathy at the state I was in.

The following day I visited the shop from which I had purchased the binoculars and asked if they would kindly look at them. Naturally, I was asked why and the assistant too had a good laugh at my expense but he tested them and found they lived up to the guarantee – shock and water resistant. Some forty years later I still have and use them after having been round the world and back again.

Daphne Butler

Bird reserves are clearly places where one would not provoke negative remarks when using binoculars. Indeed, people seem to look rather out of place at a bird reserve *without* them. Horse racing courses are another venue where binoculars are commonly seen – in fact they are *de rigueur* for some race goers. Moving on to more general geographical locations, the seaside seems still to be a place where binoculars are openly accepted and the author has often been asked by passers-by to identify distant ships or other things at sea when scanning with a binocular. In the UK it is still easy to find cheap binoculars for sale in the shops close to the sea-front in most coastal resorts. Seaside binocular use brings pitfalls for the unwary, however, as the author found out during a teenage exchange visit to the south of France (page 142). In the UK the paranoia about the risk of paedophiles has made many male binocular users uncomfortable about observing through binoculars at beaches where young children are playing – even though their interest is really out at sea. There have even been cases where individuals have been quizzed by over-concerned parents as to why they are using binoculars on the beach!

The author lives and works in a semi-urban part of England and his research for this book has caused him frequently to venture outside as he tested and compared models. Using binoculars in the vicinity of residential streets certainly arouses interest and even occasionally suspicion from local people. He is grateful that his immediate neighbours, who must have seen him peering out of windows through binoculars at all hours of the day and night, have not called the police complaining of a 'peeping Tom'.

Some people regularly use their binoculars in towns and cities to study architectural details within and outside buildings. Some even take close-focussing models into art galleries and museums for close-up views of the exhibits. Using binoculars in public places such as cities does, however, tend to provoke a reaction, with people craning their necks to see what you are looking at or even asking if there is anything exciting to see.

> *'Though not an artist, I still enjoyed viewing closely through a binocular details of the superb Michelangelo paintings high up on the ceiling of the Sistine Chapel in Rome'*
> HENRY PAUL

There have been several cases of binocular users finding themselves in hot water having used their binoculars in inappropriate locations. A high profile and newsworthy example from Europe involved a group of plane spotters who were imprisoned in Greece for using their binoculars in the vicinity of military airfields.

A curious law passed in Spain in the 1990s meant that for a short period of time it was technically illegal to watch birds through binoculars unless you had a permit from the government. This led to farcical scenes involving overseas bird-tour groups having their binoculars confiscated for watching Spain's avian wonders. The huge potential impact on tourism – not to mention the plain ridiculous nature of the law itself – meant that this peculiar piece of legislation did not last long.

Certain users sometimes 'break the rules' by using their binoculars in unusual ways. During the author's university days he used to regularly see bird fanatics at work in the main library, with their binoculars on their study desks. This allowed them to check out the species that were moving about in the trees and lawned areas outside the library windows. There were some interesting finds by birdwatchers using their binoculars in this way, together with opportunities for close-up views of some interesting species from the upper floors of the library. Inspired by these innovative binocular users, the author had to hand a compact Pentax binocular as he sat at his desk in the lofty library where this chapter was written. His 'library bird list' soon reached double figures!

MY BINOCULAR STORY

Is that a bra?

I HAVE A friend who used to teach in an infant school in Sheffield. She asked her class of 7-year-olds to do a painting of what they had done over the weekend. She was baffled by one serious little girl's painting full of people walking around with their bras on over their clothes. When questioned gently about this odd bra wearing habit, the child was deeply shocked. Two circles on the chest and a strap round the neck was her way of depicting binoculars. She had been to an RSPB bird reserve that weekend!

Phillippa Pearce

MY BINOCULAR STORY

A token gesture

FOR MANY YEARS during the 1990s, Myfanwy Jenkins took her three children on holiday to the seabird islands of Skomer and Skokholm in west Wales. She combined the holiday with some volunteering, helping to safeguard the natural heritage of the islands. One Christmas her youngest son, six, asked if he could have a binocular to take with him on holiday as he was fascinated by wildlife. Mindful of the high price of many binocular makes at the time – especially for a single mother – Myfanwy opted to take advantage of Texaco's token scheme and save up for a binocular for her son. Many tanks of petrol later, she had enough tokens to treat her son to his first binocular.

Some time later Myfanwy and her family were on the islands and the warden showed off his smart binocular. Intrigued to know more, a polite question from a boy wearing Texaco binoculars could be heard, 'How much would those cost?' The warden proudly retorted that £600 would be needed to secure such a fine binocular, only to be met by a prompt reply, 'If you'd got your petrol at Texaco then you could have got them for free!'

MY BINOCULAR STORY

I-Spy with my little eye something beginning with…

ONE DAY MY wife and I took my grandson, who was about five at the time, birdwatching. We are all very keen birdwatchers, but not quite 'twitchers'! We had bought him his first pair of binoculars and been down to Minsmere to see what we could see, very near our home here in Suffolk. On the way home we played 'I Spy' as we usually do in the car, it was his turn and the letter he chose was 'nugh' (N). We played for a long while but had to give up, to his delight. 'I've won Grandad!', he yelled. 'Alright,' I said, 'Now tell us what you saw'.

'NOCKERLERS!', he shouted.
Paul Brook

Children and binoculars

A Swift 8.5x44 Audubon binocular from the 1960s included an instruction booklet with the following wording: *'When not in use this binocular should be kept in its case and away from children.'*

How unfortunate! The authors' own experience with young children and binoculars has given rise to two simple rules: they are invariably intrigued by binoculars and want to look through them, but once they have studied both the eyepiece and objective ends, viewing the wrong way round seems much more fun! This is probably because, when used conventionally, binoculars can be hard for children to hold steady and fiddly to focus as they try to find objects through them; using them the other way round is much easier and gives them a strange far away view of the world that brings its own delights.

When introducing children to binoculars the game they all seem to want to play is to spot different people waving when looking through the objective end – the extreme wide-angle view attainable when using them in this way means that a whole room of people can all be seen in one go! Children can, of course, be taught to use binoculars properly, even at a young age. The author's own experiences as a child provide evidence of this, since he had not even reached the age of ten when he got his first good quality binocular and he spent the rest of his pre-teen years birdwatching in all conditions with it.

'Some people, when in the presence of an optical instrument, seem to be seized with an uncontrollable urge to touch a finger to the lens if it is within reach.'

Ernest Cherrington

The distinctive appearance of binoculars means that toy versions are sometimes incorporated into children's playground equipment. Many children seem to enjoy the make believe world of sighting distant ships, dragons or monsters through these brightly-coloured binoculars without lenses. Children who enjoy

Children invariably enjoy playing with binoculars, even those that are little more than toys

A child's optical toy, incorporating a simple Galilean binocular

147

MY BINOCULAR STORY

Forgiven but not forgotten

THE RSPB RESERVE at North Warren Suffolk – 1992. An early sunny spring morning, two wardens, Rob Macklin and Pete Etheridge, both dressed in the then regulation Barbour jackets and wellies with binoculars around their necks. Rob's, Zeiss Jena 10x50s, Pete's, Optolyth 10x40s.

Both wardens were fencing off a ditch separating a caravan site from the recently-acquired Church Farm marshes, a mosaic of low lying grazing meadows close to the North Sea and thus ideal for waders and wildfowl.

With a tractor and a trailer full of fence posts, wire and other fencing equipment, work had started. Rob placed his binoculars on the ground behind the tractor to avoid them being inadvertently trodden on and Pete hung his on a completed part of the fence.

Later, with another section completed, Rob asked Pete to move the tractor. After reversing a length of the vehicle, Pete noticed a leather strap sticking out of the grass and moving closer, with some trepidation, found he had reversed over his boss's binoculars. With a gentle pull, Rob's pride and joy – and being an RSPB warden his constant companion without which he felt undressed –

was released from the grass with a sucking noise leaving a perfect indent.

Getting a piece of cloth, Pete cleaned off the mud and said, 'Rob I've just reversed the tractor over your binoculars'.

'You've what!' exclaimed Rob.

'I've just run over your binoculars but they seem alright.' And they were. The large wide tyres of the trailer had gently squashed the binoculars into the wet marshy ground without damaging them. With the mud cleaned off, Rob tried them out and they were just as good as ever. Pete was forgiven, but didn't live it down for years.

MY BINOCULAR STORY

Where has all the fungus gone?

IN 1981 I was vacationing in the US Virgin Islands and decided to check out the stores in Charlotte, Amalia, looking specifically for a pair of binoculars. I don't remember all the brands and models I auditioned, but I'm guessing my price range was between $50 to $100. A salesman mentioned that he had a pre-owned pair that he could show me. He brought out a pair of mint Zeiss West Germany 8x30Bs. I distinctly

remember my feeling of relief at finally discovering great optics – almost liberating…I was blown away. The salesman mentioned these Zeiss binoculars had a bit of peripheral fungus, which was barely noticeable, both to me and my travelling companion. Though they were caseless, and $100, I took the chance. I remember chartering a sailboat later that day, and I was unable to peel these beauties away from my face: the seagulls, the islands, THE OPTICS… I was hooked. Well you never forget

your first Zeiss. I made it home to Colorado and back to reality. I don't know if it was the next time I picked up the Zeiss, or thirty times later, but the fungus was gone! The dry Colorado air had evaporated it. Fast forward to last September, I decided to go on eBay to search for an original case for my 8x30s, and check their current value. I finally found an original case in mint condition, with the original cardboard box that has the designation 8x30B.

Roy Bloomfield

using binoculars can also read a range of story books about people and their binoculars – *Bernies' Big Blue Binoculars* and *The Magic Binoculars* are two examples of the more intriguing titles to choose from.

Repairing and serving

From time to time binocular owners need to call upon the services of skilled technicians to rectify any problems that are afflicting their instruments. The most common complaint is probably that the binocular goes out of alignment (technically speaking out of 'collimation'), meaning that the two binocular barrels do not point in exactly the same direction. The deterioration in optical performance caused by the build up of haze or dust on the internal glass surfaces is also a common problem, especially in older binoculars.

Unfortunately, in common with many of the more developed nations, the UK is witnessing a decline in the number of people who are qualified in specific trades that require the skilled use of the hands as well as the head. It has become increasingly difficult, for example, to find suitably-qualified tradespeople to fix household matters such as electrical difficulties or plumbing problems. This dearth in those skilled with their hands has touched the world of binoculars, so much so that the repair and servicing of binoculars can even be considered a dying trade in many parts of the world. In the UK, the number of highly-skilled binocular repairers can be counted on the fingers of two hands.

This phenomenon has led to difficulties for collectors and people with damaged binoculars in finding technicians to put these optical devices back into use. It does not help that a perfectly decent binocular can be bought in budget supermarkets such as Lidl for as little as £10, when the cost of re-aligning a

Inexpensive pocket binoculars are a popular souvenir acquired by young visitors to the Imperial War Museum in London. The inscription 'spy glasses' has been added to this model to create a sense of connection with past users of miniature binoculars during times of war

Optrep, a British company run by Tony Kay, is one of the last in the country specialising in the repair and servicing of optical instruments. Prior to setting up his repair business, Tony was the proprietor of Kay Optical, the London-based optical sales company which is still run by his son (➧ page 169).

MY BINOCULAR STORY

Life as a binocular boy

BINOCULARS WERE THE start of my lifelong interest in optics and I still have great affection for them. I was at the Grand National horse race at Aintree when I was about eight and somebody I knew let me look through their binos – wow! It blew my mind to see all these horses so close up.

I was an indentured apprentice 'Instrument Maker' at Elliotts Liverpool Ltd from 1954 to 1959, leaving as a 'Tradesman' in about 1960. When I was about 18 or so I moved from marine instrument repairs to binocular repairs and did that for about a year – a position known as 'binocular boy'.

The job entailed anything to do with the repair and servicing of binoculars of all makes and types, 99% of them prismatic types. We did binocular and telescope repairs for all the opticians and camera shops in Liverpool, and all sorts of makes and models turned up – from Kershaw to Zeiss. There were also lots of military surplus models from the UK, USA and Germany.

We generally didn't like any French binos as they tended to have very fancy shaped bodies. One in particular I remember looked like a butterfly when you looked down on the eyepiece end and this made it awkward to remove, refit and adjust the prisms.

We handled a lot of material from Sewell's, who were a very active ships' provider of instruments in Liverpool and used to bring all the repairs they collected on their ship visits to us at Elliotts. That included binos, sextants, Walker's ships logs, Aldis lamps and manual fog horns. The latter were often damaged as they were a favourite place for the crew to hide their contraband.

Straightforward collimation of binos that had been knocked/dropped was very common. I also was trained to completely strip them down, clean prisms of fungus and dirt before rebuilding them and to repair and lubricate focus drives.

We also had to make parts when necessary. Times were

tough, money tight and people would pay for repairs rather than throw things away as they do today. For instance we made on the lathe new cells and the eccentric adjusting rings for the bino objectives.

One common problem with older binos was the appearance of 'stars' in the objective lens This was caused by the cement (often Canada Balsam in those days) starting to deteriorate. We had to carefully bring these lenses to the boil in water and then with 'asbestos fingers' we would separate the elements while still very hot, clean off the old cement, put in new cement and manipulate the lens to get rid of any air bubbles. Finally we mated them together and then cooked them in an oven to cause the cement solvent to evaporate before refitting them to their respective cells.

One of my friends had to remove some 'stars' from an objective lens as described above. As it was late Friday

afternoon he decided he would soak the lens in some solvent over the weekend rather than the quicker 'boil it' method. To say he was rather upset on the Monday morning to find that the lens had disappeared is to understate the problem. The lens was some war time production which was made of plastic rather than glass and had dissolved in the solvent!

Making eyepiece shrouds was very common, first screwcutting them in a lathe and then with hand tools like a wood turner, we would shape them on a lathe to match the 'non damaged' one of the pair. If both were damaged we 'designed' our own.

We also replaced the worn out leather covering on the binos. We did this by cutting out the required shapes from thin leather sheets and glueing them (with fish glue in a warm pot! – no super glue in those days), stretching and moulding them to the body of the binos in the process..Of course we resprayed

them to finish them off. We resprayed lots of our repaired binos to make them look like a really good job, which they did.

We did have lots of fun as apprentices, even though Elliotts employed lots of us as cheap labour. I started in 1954 on two pounds eight shillings a week (a Zeiss West 8x30 binocular cost over £50 new in England at that time). I will not mention names in the episode where we set the railway embankment on fire by test firing an old 'horse pistol' we had refurbished!

One memory that always makes me smile concerns telescope repairs, Liverpool being a port with lots of ships. One telescope that came in for repair came from the props manager of one of Liverpool's theatres. There was an 'I see no ships'-type scene in this play where the leading actor puts a telescope up to his eye and pulls out the draw tube to supposedly focus the scope, and unfortunately for him the interior

stop ring had come unscrewed and the tube came completely out and he ended up with a black eye!

In 1968 I left the UK and after four years in Switzerland headed to New Zealand where I set up what is now the country's longest established company specialising in the sales and service of surveying-type instruments. We dealt with a few binoculars but tended to use the services of two specialists, one in Wellington and the other in Auckland, as their rates were much lower than ours.

We are now lucky enough to live on the edge of Lake Taupo, in the centre of North Island. I am a keen fisherman and the lake is a famous trout fishery. From my house I can see the particular spot where I do most of my fly fishing to check out who is fishing there. When things are 'hot' fish-wise I can see without leaving my lounge where the trout are as they leap about.

Pete Kinsella

binocular is likely to be £50! Although attractive to the consumer, this has also fuelled the throwaway culture that pervades everyday life today.

It is a source of considerable concern to binocular enthusiasts that there appear to be so few young people learning the trade of instrument repair. This is happening in the UK despite government efforts to put apprenticeships of a variety of kinds back on the career map. The modern high-tech world of computers or the more lucrative trade in domestic services seem like much more attractive propositions for most young people. The present trajectory of decline in binocular technicians suggests that by 2020 – when the current generation has retired – it may be impossible to find any independent companies offering this vital service.

Perhaps the last place where binocular technicians are still being trained is within the prestigious European and Japanese companies which offer comprehensive guarantees and service commitments to customers. Here, in specially prepared clean rooms, highly-skilled individuals in white coats carry out repairs and servicing work to very high standards (► see box)

Some enthusiasts inevitably dabble with binocular repairs, to varying degrees of success. While the overhaul and cleaning of Galilean instruments is reasonably straightforward, as soon as prisms are added to the mix things quickly get rather complicated. The correct alignment of these binoculars, in particular, can prove a very tricky task. The author has optimistically taken apart several prismatic models – even carefully labelling each part – only to find the correct reassembly to be a task too far. He now tends to leave that to the experts.

Simple Galilean binoculars, which do not contain complex prism systems, are much easier to take apart, clean and reassemble – a task sometimes carried out by their owners. Prismatic binoculars, by contrast, tend to be the preserve of professional technicians

BINOCULAR TECHNICIANS AT LEICA CAMERA

An interview with Jörg Kaufmann, division manager for customer service at Leica Camera AG, Germany

How is the training of binocular technicians at Leica organised?

Skilled workers are employed in Leica repair workshops around the world. They begin their training by learning something about the history of the Leica factory and a variety of products – not just binoculars. They then spend time with departments which are involved in product development and production, after which they learn how to assemble and disassemble binoculars. All technicians must understand how and why different parts of a product work together. If they can understand this system, they will learn to define malfunctions and the reason for these.

Are there different levels of technician?

There are three types of technicians: junior technicians (those in training), technicians (those who repair different products) and senior technicians (those who instruct other technicians). We have four technicians who are working permanently on binocular repairs and four as back-up, two junior and two senior technicians. It takes up to three years to reach the grade of junior technician and up to seven years for become a technician. Those colleagues who are senior technicians have at least 10 years' experience and some have over 20.

What qualifications are needed for technicians?

They must have an education as a skilled engineering worker to be considered. Senior technicians are educated to Masters level.

How easy is it to find suitable people for these jobs?

It is very difficult to find people on the free market with the skills we need, so Leica educates people for its own requirements, but it is a very complex operation.

What kinds of repairs can Leica carry out?

We are able to repair virtually any product Leitz/Leica has ever sold. We have workshops all over the world, including the USA, UK, France, Hong Kong, Japan, Australia and South Africa. All workshops work only with original Leica spare parts which we have in stock in a very large warehouse. This means we have 20,000 different parts and about 5,000,000 single components for our full range of products.

The Ultravid 10x42 BR

IMAGE: LEICA CAMERA AG, SOLMS, GERMANY

8 Collecting

Although binocular collecting remains a minority pastime compared with the large numbers of people attracted to cameras, it is nonetheless a passionate hobby for those who get bitten by the bug. It is a world of fine optical glass, landmark models and of course special rarities. This chapter lifts the veil on that world. It shows how at a time when the second-hand binocular market was drying up, the 21st century phenomenon of eBay rekindled interest in the often obscure world of optics. The chapter also introduces the little-known and sometimes bizarre topic of binoculars without lenses, where you might find such treasures as a teddy bear sporting felt binoculars or an aftershave set housed in a hollow binocular flask. Welcome to the wonderful world of binocular collecting.

Advertising material, such as this atmospheric offering from Carl Zeiss Jena, was originally produced for display in shops. Now that the company no longer exists, they are prized collectors' items, as this proud binocular enthusiast can testify

Prismen-
feldstecher

'Collecting binoculars is
like collecting history'
PETER HUNT

COLLECTING SEEMS TO be an innate human compulsion. Across continents and over centuries people from different cultures and social backgrounds have collected the beautiful, valuable or intriguing. But what is the precise allure of binoculars – and why are binocular collectors almost always *men*?

Somebody can be said to possess a binocular collection if they have more binoculars than they might need for their own day to day use. While a person with wide ranging hobbies – and bulging pockets – might legitimately possess five or more binoculars (including spares), they enter the ranks of the collector as soon as they acquire an instrument that, when put to a specific use, is inferior to any binocular they already possess.

It is likely that there have been binocular collectors almost as long as there have been binoculars themselves. Modern binocular collections vary in size from a dozen or so examples to vast arrays which would take several days to look through. Most serious binocular enthusiasts put together collections that number at least 30 and often extend into the low hundreds, a figure capped by storage limitations in their homes as well as their bank balance. However, some collectors have amassed over a thousand binoculars. Why so many? Quite simply, it seems, because collecting optics can so easily become an addiction and obsession.

'My wife is a binocular widow and curses the arrival of each new pair. She just does not understand the fascination. I also collect Great War memorabilia and found a lovely pair of Zeiss 6x30 Marineglass inscribed to a friend of Rommel. Nice to use as well!'

BRITISH COLLECTOR

Some binocular enthusiasts enjoy amassing a collection that represents a sample of all the makes and models ever produced. Others choose to concentrate their efforts on one type of binocular (e.g. those used by the military) or a specific brand (e.g. Leica, Zeiss or Swift). Some, however, focus on a finer sample: binoculars made in the UK, used at sea or offering wide-angle views, for example. Other people amass collections for special purposes, for example as film props, re-enactment tools or in historical research. The author's reference collection of over 500 binoculars – which is now slowly being sold off – certainly falls into this category.

A binocular collection represents a perfect example of a collection that is both useable and attractive to have on the shelf. With a little internal cleaning binoculars made even over a hundred years ago are perfectly useable today. Indeed, the impressive performance of very early prismatic binoculars often comes as a surprise to those who have paid high prices for their state-of-the-art 21st century optics. Many binocular collectors actually use their binoculars, at least from time to time – they do not just gather dust on the shelf or in the display case. A few, however, choose to keep them in completely original condition, refusing to open them to bring them into good optical order. This is especially the case with collectors of

WHY DO YOU COLLECT BINOCULARS?

'I simply have a nerdish obsession with the things. I sell on to make room for more, and with increasing knowledge also buy to sell.'

British collector

'In the past I've collected bins and then sold the lot but my now "fetish" has returned!'

British collector

'I love the feeling of history that comes with them. When you look through them, it's incredible to think what people might have seen who have also used them.'

British collector

'I enjoy collecting the military binoculars of the major armed forces, and comparing the different models.'

Chinese collector

'Collecting binoculars is like collecting history.'

British collector

'I like the sense of craftsmanship that has gone into them and the fact that they are still useable even 100 years after they were made.'

British collector

'I love big binoculars which I use for astronomy and for the view over the ocean from my house in Macau'

Chinese collector

'My interest comes from my dad: he was always interested in them and had some nice World War II surplus pairs. Since he passed away 10 years ago, I've also taken to collecting and selling them. They do seem to me the nearest thing to magic I can think of!'

British collector

'I am retiring from the police service this year due to a knee injury and have spent most of the year at home. In April I realised that I owned ten pairs of binoculars. That's when my binocular collection became binocular collecting. The time off has given me the ability to research and learn and I now have over 70 pairs.'

Australian collector

'I love collecting binoculars because there's so much to discover. Just when you think you've got the measure of a particular brand or model, something new comes along to surprise you.'

British collector

military binoculars. The restoration of binoculars is, however, vital when comparative judgements on the performance of similar models need to be made.

> *'Remember that I said that it's a bad idea to keep fungally-infected binoculars with non-infected ones? Well, I think I must have caught something, because I caught myself eyeing up second-hand binoculars in a shop window yesterday! I was interested to note that there was a pair of 3x spectacle bins too!'*
>
> ANDY HAY, COMMENTING ON THE EARLY STAGE OF A BINOCULAR COLLECTOR'S PASSION

Most binocular collectors are fond of optics produced for military use, in part because so many innovative designs were made, including many of the finest models ever manufactured. Military binoculars also frequently bring with them intriguing history concerning their use in war, bear unusual codes and markings or are rare to find. For this reason military binoculars have acquired special status

THE AUTHOR'S FAVOURITE BINOCULARS

MY OWN REFERENCE collection as I worked on this book amounted to over 500 different binoculars. I felt I needed to buy so many because during a brief encounter with a binocular in a shop or a fleamarket it is not possible to test fully the quality of the instrument – that needs to take place outdoors, in a variety of lighting and weather conditions. So I made the decision to actually own very many binoculars, some for a few weeks and others for more than a year. This allowed me to make lengthy comparisons between different makes and models in all conditions, even taking some examples overseas.

I was, however, determined not keep a large collection in perpetuity: I am not fundamentally a collector, rather I needed a reference collection to complete this written overview, and I would rather spend the money on other essential items in the long term. As I started to sell off the instruments in the reference collection, the question of which models I would keep for day to day use was uppermost in my mind. My varied hobbies mean that I can justifiably keep a wider range of binoculars than many people and still use them most weeks. I finally settled on keeping five models, which suit my needs and pocket best. It is not an accident that two are also featured in their own 'Landmark binocular' panels. I want to place

on record here the fact that it is extremely difficult to make a final selection for a handful of models when you have tested so many different types of binocular. The result of all this testing is that you have become acquainted with all the best features from countless models, and there is simply no binocular in existence that now ticks every box!

Sport/theatre/opera use

Bushnell Custom 6x25 – no longer made and not well known outside the USA, it is much less common than its larger cousin the 7x26, but provides superbly bright and colour-faithful wide-angle viewing in a tiny package. The earlier model came with a wonderfully cute black leather case. Its small size makes it perfect for popping in the pocket.

Nature watching – compacts

Pentax Papillio 6.5x21 – combines the ability to view distant subjects with extreme close focus (50 cm), making it ideal for anybody interested in insects as well as birds and mammals. Though there are compact models with finer resolution

for many collectors. U-boat binoculars, for example, continue to have an irresistible allure, and those binoculars used by German forces under the direction of Adolf Hitler, complete with their swastika insignia, are among the most sought after. Many had their markings obliterated after the war and those that survived are now banned from sale in Germany. The demands of the military also meant that optical quality and robustness were sometimes more important than cost, providing collectors with the opportunity to own useable instruments today that would have cost governments a small fortune when new.

Part of the author's own pleasure in using some of the war time binoculars in his reference collection is to give a new life to instruments whose use was previously intertwined with conflict. For example, he has used a German 10x80 stand-mounted binocular for astronomy, while being fully aware that this same instrument may have been used to spot incoming British aircraft over Germany,

(e.g. the Nikon 8x20 HG), the dual near and far use of the Papillio is unmatched by any other manufacturer at the time of writing. [▶ see also page 93]

Nature watching – full size

Canon 10x30 image stabilised – even without the image stabilisation feature this binocular shows itself to be a supreme performer, with razor sharp definition and faithful colour rendition. Canon's superb super spectra coating renders images of such brightness that it seems unbelievable that this binocular has objectives of only 30 mm in diameter. When the stabilisation button is pressed, the effect is spectacular and makes identification of hitherto unrecognisable animals possible. [▶ see also page 74]

Astronomy

Celestron 15x70 Skymaster – this model, more than any I have used, shows what modern Chinese production is capable of. Side by side comparisons with expensive 15x models by Zeiss and Swarovski reveal the Celestron to be

outstanding value for money. I use this model tripod mounted for wide-angle views of the night sky.

Long distance terrestrial observation

Telescope Service 20x88 – the location of my home in the Yorkshire Dales affords me long distance views of the valleys and hills, making a large stand mounted binocular worthwhile. The Telescope Service model is actually designed for astronomy with its 90 degree angled eyepieces, but I find the quality of the image to be the best of any x20 binocular I have looked through. It also comes with x26 and x32 drop in eyepieces for viewing extra detail.

BB

with a view to shooting them down. While some people may despise objects that have clearly been used in anger against others (as they do with guns and other weapons), some binocular enthusiasts enjoy giving them a fresh, more positive second life. And the spectacular views obtained through 10x80 binoculars of comet Holmes show what new treasures await those prepared to experiment.

Another important part of putting together a collection is without doubt the joy that comes with finding an old object preserved in near new condition; and for binoculars the feeling that you may have been the first person to look through an instrument since it was stored away and forgotten about many decades ago. That joy is made all the more tangible when original paperwork – instruction books, guarantees and even receipts – are found with the binocular. Hand-written receipts from the days before electronic tills are a particular pleasure, and help to cast light on the comparatively high cost of binoculars in the past.

FOUR COLLECTABLE BINOCULARS WITH A HISTORY

Whose binocular?

This Argentine army-issued 6x30 binocular was brought back as a souvenir from the 1982 Falklands War, but was actually made in Leeds, UK, by the firm Kershaw.

Political theory

A Zeiss Deltrintem dating from 1932 and marked on the prism plate 'Hon K G Younger'. A small British military arrow has been added to the other prism plate, suggesting it was donated and used in the British war effort during World War II. Younger, who came from a famous British brewing family, was a member of the 1958 Labour government which encouraged moves towards more trade with Europe. The binocular was housed in a canvas military case with the name 'Captain S W Wren' written inside, an officer who served in both world wars.

Rare find

This Fuji Brothers Victor No.3 binocular was made early in World War I by the company that would eventually become Nikko and thence Nikon. Found in a loft in England, it is thought to be one of the only known examples in the world.

Service rendered

A World War I Zeiss London British army binocular which is marked on the case lid 'Off USA airman for service rendered 1942 on crashed fortress'. The case (an American Bausch & Lomb version) is marked on the top 'W Shakeshaft RAF'.

Binoculars are fundamentally for seeing and many binocular collectors seem to be interested in getting better views of the world – whatever their particular interests. Most enjoy colour, light and landscape and use binoculars to explore this fascinating world in more detail. Many have specific observing interests, but all would still happily spend an hour or two looking through a sample of binoculars, enjoying the subtleties of light as conditions alter and comparing performance. In this sense, many binocular collectors are seemingly united by their passion for *looking*. Those who collect binoculars frequently liken their interactions with them as 'playful', as they look through different makes and models. Returning to a binocular that has not been used for a while can be like meeting an old friend again, with a shared history between owner and user.

A fascination for many binocular collectors is to wonder what sights have been witnessed through instruments that can span many centuries. Since the binocular was invented technology has transformed the world in ways unimaginable to those of times past. Binoculars allow one to focus – quite literally – on just one part of the world at one moment in time, but generations may have peered through that same binocular and seen things wonderful, or indeed horrific. If only a binocular could record what has been seen through it. It is not surprising to learn, therefore, that binocular collectors also tend have a keen interest in history.

'It is possible to enjoy using a 1930s binocular with a pleasure akin to that derived from motoring in a car of the same era.'
ROBERT GREGORY

MY BINOCULAR STORY

Old friends

WHEN AT HOME Steve Kirk always keeps his binocular (a Bausch & Lomb 10x40 Custom) by the kitchen window, ready to study any birds visiting his garden, near Bristol. He describes his binoculars as his 'old friend'.

Steve has been a member of the RSPB for 50 years and loves birdwatching. He had, therefore, been looking forward to some trips out during a visit to see his daughter in Norfolk, home to many of England's finest nature reserves. The bags were packed and he set out with his wife on the long journey from the west to east coast. On arrival at Norwich station confusion resulted in the couple getting on the wrong train heading for Nottingham rather than the one

for Sheringham. With seconds to spare, Steve whipped their bags off the Nottingham train and they just managed to board to Sheringham-bound locomotive before it left for North Norfolk.

Relief, then horror as Steve realised that he had left his small backpack – with his wallet and his binocular – on the Nottingham train! On arrival in Sheringham a series of frantic calls to rail staff resulted in the promise of his bag, found when the train arrived in Nottingham, to be collected the next day in Norwich. Sure enough the bag returned from its excursion in one piece, but there was no binocular, and the cash had been removed from his wallet.

Steve spent a frustrating week on holiday, trying to watch

birds without any optical aids. He couldn't wait to get home in order to make an insurance claim for the binocular.

The following week, he was sitting in his kitchen and a small bird attracted his attention in the garden. Automatically, he put his hand to the window sill where his binocular would usually be kept and lifted it to his eyes. What! This is the very binocular he thought he had left on a train bound for Nottingham! It was only at this moment – much to the amusement of his wife – that Steve realised that the binocular had never even been packed for the Norfolk trip. His old friend was there by the kitchen window, waiting for his return.

BB

Another sensory pleasure of a binocular collection is the wonderful aroma that some instruments give off, which is usually imparted by their luxurious leather cases. Smell can trigger memories in a powerful way, and the author only has to lift his Carl Zeiss Jena 10x50 binocular to his face to be taken back to his teenage years as a birdwatcher. This unexpected sensory dimension to a binocular collection is confirmed by many collectors. There are even binocular enthusiasts who can name the manufacturer of a binocular just from its aroma – rather like a fine wine!

'Binocular field glasses form a relatively modern target-topic for collectors. Students of technology discovered their history even more recently.'

WILLIAM REID

Pin badges allow binocular collectors to show their colours

Binocular collectors are often quite technically minded and enjoy the design innovations that have occurred in this particular branch of optics. Some have learnt to repair and overhaul binoculars – either through their profession or as part of an engrossing hobby – and use their skills to delve inside interiors to gain a better understanding of prisms and lens arrangements. Prisms are wonderful jewel-like objects in their own right, with mysterious abilities to bend light and create indoor rainbows. They have their own fascination and are sometimes collected for their intrinsic value (➧ see box).

MY BINOCULAR STORY

MY BINOCULAR STORY

Collecting prisms

WHEN I WAS approximately six-years-old in about 1943, I lived in the Harehills district of Leeds. One of the most treasured possessions of local children were the prisms which were taken from the rubbish dump in the yard of the nearby Kershaw optical factory. During the manufacture of prisms (Kershaw had a contract to produce binoculars for the war effort) there must have been a high failure rate, and the rejected prisms were cast onto the dump, to be found by adventurous boys who climbed over the fence in search of booty!

These jewel-like prisms were prized items and a status symbol among boys at my school. I got hold of one by swapping it for something and kept it safe in a drawer at home. They used to be shown around the boys at my school, lights were shone through them and they attracted a lot of interest.

Life was, of course, very different in those times. Rationing was in full force and there was not much in the shops. We used to see planes flying overhead and me and my friend could tell which the German ones were because of the different note of their engines.

I remember seeing a Luftwaffe map of Leeds, highlighting the areas that were targets in aerial bombardments. The nearby Burton clothing factory, which supplied military uniforms, was clearly highlighted, as was the Ditchburn aircraft factory, but I don't remember seeing the Kershaw factory singled out.

I am now 70 and live on the south coast in a downland village near Beachy Head. My main hobby is birdwatching. I am amused that the cost of my Swarovski EL bins would have bought a pair of newly-built semi-detached houses when my parents moved in to Harehills in the early 1930s.

Cyril Burwell

Although there are a few international clubs and societies for binocular collectors, at the more local or even country level, such organisations are rather rare. As a result it is much more likely to find informal gatherings of binocular enthusiasts. Many collectors are also in touch with others by email and the telephone, and most weeks lively correspondence takes place concerning new finds, technical details of models and instruments on 'transfer lists'. Among collecting friends it is common practice to allow binoculars to change hands without adding on any additional profit. An important email newsletter is issued with considerable frequency to serious collectors and enthusiasts, its archives providing the most detailed internet source on the history of binoculars.

Binocular collectors have sometimes been called 'kind eccentrics' – a characterisation that the author can relate to. Many are warm, generous with their knowledge and eager to share their enthusiasm with others. Only a tiny minority seem to be difficult to engage with, secretive, or feel the need to prove their 'expertise' to others at every opportunity. This is not to say that collectors don't like to catch film makers out by spotting historical or other inaccuracies on the movie screen. The author found himself playing this game when watching the classic British war-time comedy *Dad's Army*, the film version of which begins with German army officers scanning the horizon with what is clearly a Barr & Stroud CF41 binocular – standard issue to British naval forces!

'Instead of relaxing with a pipe or a cigar…I find diversion in comparing similar glasses of different ages, in whatever light conditions prevail.'

Robert Gregory

Some collectors get a little carried away with their finds. Here, a mug has been commissioned with the insignia of The North Irish Horse, a military unit in which a previous owner of the binocular pictured served during World War I. The mug includes a dedication to this former soldier

Curiously, given the accessibility and appeal of binocular collecting as outlined above, serious binocular collectors seem to be something of a scarce breed. There are believed to be less than a hundred in the whole of the UK. This is especially striking when one considers the number of people who collect similar objects such as cameras, for example. Binocular collectors are vastly outnumbered by people who are merely enthusiastic about binoculars, yet possess only a small number – perhaps just one – for day to day use.

Many binocular collectors enjoy testing different binoculars to determine comparative performance. This is frequently a social activity which brings collectors together, sometimes in sizeable groups, to carry out tests on specific models or types of binocular. The binocular resources of several collectors are often pooled during these gatherings, often bringing together a wider range of models than any one collector would possess. Military testing charts are often used during these kind of tests to compare resolution at various distances, and under different lighting conditions.

INTERVIEW WITH A BINOCULAR COLLECTOR

CHRIS ROBINSON, A retired accountant with a pension adequate enough to support his love of all things optical, is a binocular collector. His earliest memories involved playing, as a child, with magnifying glasses, a small brass telescope for train spotting and a Boer War Galilean field glass given to him by his grandfather. His first binocular was a 7x50 Ross Steplux, bought second-hand from Dollond & Aitchison in Leeds, the city where Chris was born. He bought this shortly after he entered articles when he was 16 and he still has this particular binocular.

A love of train spotting in the late 1950s and early 1960s really made him want a good binocular but he couldn't afford them then. By the time he could afford them, steam trains had gone but the bug had bitten and he has stayed bitten ever since.

Chris is also interested in model engineering and has a small workshop so he can repair instruments. The two interests, optics and engineering, go very well together. He has a collection of over 200 vintage binoculars of which one third are properly aligned and the rest are not. For Chris, the attraction of binoculars is the sheer tactile design, accuracy and usefulness of the things. There are limitless designs and variations for the collector, they hold their value and even non-enthusiasts can hold them, use them and appreciate their weight and beauty.

Among Chris's favourite binoculars are:

- Four examples of Hensoldt Dialyt roof prism binoculars from 1950 to 1970 (16x56, 8x56, 6x42 and 6x30) all in pristine condition, clear and aligned. A wonderful lightweight glass in Chris's view.
- A Negretti & Zambra 8x30 from about 1920 which Chris thinks is a well made glass with a surprisingly wide field. Though easy to look through the previous owner, a navy officer, must have smoked strong dark shag tobacco. The nicotine took hours to remove from the leather and smoke has got inside giving the optics an unnatural yellow tint.

Nonetheless a favourite user glass for Chris because of the wide field and he also loves the smell!

- Zeiss West 20x60 image stabilised. Chris considers this a mechanical and optical marvel but admits that it is heavy.
- Various early Carl Zeiss Jena Feldstecher x8 models from about 1897 to 1900. Chris revels in the beautiful hand-made quality of these binoculars as well as the ability of these binoculars to still be perfectly useable after 100+ years. These are as sharp as any other binocular in his collection but lack the wide field of the later varieties with wide-angle eyepieces.
- Ross 5x40 Mark V, produced for the air ministry – a fixed focus, coated glass from late WW11 and the early 1950s. Once the focus was adjusted for his eyes he found this a great glass, which is sharp to the edges and with a wide field. Chris notes that Charles Frank in Glasgow were selling these in their 1965 war surplus catalogue at £12 10 shillings and 6 pence.

Chris enjoys trying to carry out the alignment of binoculars in his workshop – for some models it is relatively easy, for others it is much more tricky. Most of the problems are caused by slight prism displacement and removing them, cleaning the seat and prism and repacking the seating strap cures the problem. Getting into the binocular without damage in the first place is often the hardest part!

As for particular types or models in his collection, classic vintage predominates simply because of the optical quality, craftsmanship and the fact that Chris can repair them more easily than modern ones. However, he likes any good sharp or unusual binocular made before about 1975. The obvious exceptions are the Zeiss, a Canon stabilised binocular and the 7x50 Fujinons – all are exceptional examples of modern design.

For most binocular collectors, the quest for catalogues, leaflets and other advertising material tends to go hand in hand with the acquisition of optical instruments themselves. Scarce early examples of trade catalogues, especially from premium makers – can command a surprisingly high price – sometimes as much as a binocular itself! Sometimes large posters or even shop advertising signs survive, and these are eagerly snapped up to adorn the walls of collectors.

Contemporary brochures help binocular enthusiasts learn more about vintage models that are no longer made

> *'The value of use and sum of all the benefits, however, cannot explain the fascination of a good binocular, as clear today as 100 years ago.'*
>
> HANS SEEGER

Finally, we turn briefly to what the author calls the 'gender conundrum' in binocular collecting. Despite giving it considerable attention the author has failed to uncover the precise reasons why female binocular collectors (and indeed enthusiasts) are so rare. However, it is possible that – accepting the gross generalisation – because men tend to be attracted to objects which are useful and women things that are decorative, binoculars hold a special appeal for males. That is perhaps why such hobbies as camera and gramophone collecting tend to be rather male preserves too. Many binocular collectors interviewed for this book also expressed an interest in collecting other 'useful' objects, though the usefulness of model railways can rightly be disputed!

Very occasionally, stamps featuring binoculars come to the attention of collectors

Buying considerations

Many makes of binocular can still be picked up for what would be considered bargain prices when they were new, making a collection within the financial reach of many working people in more affluent countries. Indeed, binocular collectors frequently speak of the joy of purchasing, at reasonable price, a carefully-crafted vintage optical instrument that would have originally cost a doctor a month of his salary. The exception would seem to be models made by

BELOW: Original paperwork associated with binoculars adds considerably to the enjoyment of a collection. Pictured here is an original hand-written receipt from 1930 for a Hensoldt binocular sold in Munich

LEFT: Binocular testing is a feature of enthusiasts' gatherings. Here observers have assembled a wide range of instruments for comparative purposes

MY BINOCULAR STORY

The happy binocular

I'VE OFTEN WONDERED whether my binoculars should be regarded as tools or toys. Well, of course it depends. If binoculars were to be indispensable for my daily bread, my standard of living, my life, I think I would call them tools. If I were to use them only occasionally, let's say while walking the dog, I'd probably consider them toys.

Also, I think it's dependent on the binoculars' appearance. Some look very much like tools; they hardly could be anything else. Whereas others are so exquisitely toy-like, I would feel sorry for them being used more seriously. Happily, a lot of binoculars of today are both good tools and toys. But it wasn't always like that.

Before WWII, let alone during WWII, many larger binoculars were tools. They were made for warfare or hunting and they looked – and felt – like it. Then

something changed, gradually at first, then more rapidly, until suddenly we realized binoculars could be toys – and we bought them for that.

Now, history is a process, and so every appointed moment or milestone is a simplification, but I think the introduction of the Leitz Trinovid series of binoculars in 1963 is of special significance here. Optically on par, or very close to the porro binoculars' resolution of that time, these roof prism binoculars excelled in compactness, low weight and, especially, sheer beautiful overall design.

The key word was *elegance*, something not often associated with binoculars until then. Nothing about their lines and construction reminded one of the hunt, war, or anything else usually associated with manliness. On

the contrary, they were remarkably feminine in appearance.

What's even more remarkable is that they were dreamed up in the late 1950s, in a rather conservative society, still constrained by the war years. All those new ideas about cultural and personal identity we now associate with the 1960s – freedom to explore one's potential, of personal expression, of love of nature – were still a long way off. And yet, the designers at Leitz must have sensed something was in the air. They started designing something really advanced, something beyond most people's imagination. Only when people saw the Trinovids they suddenly realized that this was what they wanted all along.

Those Trinovids, I think, are the happiest binoculars in history.

Renze de Vries

IMAGE: RENZE DE VRIES

Leitz (now named Leica) and Zeiss which often come with a premium price tag as well as a distinguished heritage.

Rarity usually adds greatly to the value of objects which are collected and certain very scarce binoculars certainly fall into this category. The Ross Vanguard 7x56 represents such an example, as it is thought to have been made only in tiny numbers in Britain immediately after World War II for officers serving on HMS *Vanguard*, the last battleship to be built for the Royal Navy. An example sold recently for £2,500 on eBay. It is interesting to note that its high value today is not related to its outstanding optical performance – there were several other 7x50 war time binoculars that outperformed it. In 1998 £140,000 plus buyer's premium was paid for a superb binocular telescope made for an aristocrat by the 18th century master craftsman Pietro Patroni.

Binoculars linked to famous people tend to sell for premium prices. In April 2008 an early Zeiss 7.5x binocular was sold on UK eBay that formerly belonged to Warrington Baden-Powell, the founder of the sea scouts. The addition of a well-known name to an already desirable glass pushed its selling price easily above £300.

A prominent figure from the Japanese navy, Admiral Heihachiro Togo, is partly responsible for the high price of the wonderful Zeiss x5-x10 'revolver glass', produced in small numbers in the first decade of the 20th century. Togo, whose binocular-sporting statue can still be seen alongside the restored flagship Mikasa in the Tokosuka Naval Base, went on record to say that his revolver binocular had played a major role in a key battle during the historic victory against the Russian Baltic Fleet in the Russo-Japanese war of 1905. To this day, this innovative glass is frequently referred to as the 'Togo binocular', and visitors to the Mikasa museum can even see the original binocular on display.

The binocular collector does not have to wrestle with the problem of fakes as much as those who specialise in many other types of antiques and collectibles. The requirement for high-grade optical glass – which is both difficult to work and expensive to produce – means that any binocular purporting to be from one of the major makers would quickly belie its inferior nature as soon as the instrument was lifted to the eyes of the collector. However, this does not mean that they are never found and binocular fakes often bring with them special stories of their own (▶ see box).

It has become increasingly difficult in recent years, however, to find a wide range of second-hand binoculars in retail outlets in the UK. This has no doubt been due in part to the decline in the amount of optical military surplus coming on to the market since the 1970s. In the first two decades following the end of World War II a binocular enthusiast could easily spend a day touring the numerous shops in London where used optics could be found in abundance.

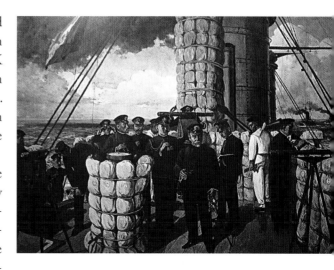

Admiral Togo on the bridge of the Mikasa, before the Battle of Tsushima in 1905. Various optical instruments can be seen in this painting, with the person directly behind the Admiral using a rangefinder

Antique shops occasionally contain binoculars which are of interest to collectors, though it can be hard work sifting through thousands of unrelated items

Who are you kidding?

This small binocular is a Zeiss fake, which was most likely engraved in Japan shortly after the end of World War II when European binoculars were highly sought after. Close observation of the engraving reveals subtle differences in letter style and logo from the usual Carl Zeiss Jena markings. This model is also marked '8x24 Silvarem', a dual error since Zeiss never made a model of this precise specification and the binocular is actually of x6 magnification. There is a certain irony in the desire to pass-off this former war-time 6x24 Japanese officer's glass as a Zeiss model, since it has a wider angle than any x6 Zeiss model made at the time and its optical quality is at least equal to the best x6 models coming off the Zeiss production line in the late 1940s

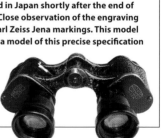

Unfortunately only one major outlet survived into the 21st century: the idiosyncratic 'Kay Optical' emporium on the southern outskirts of Greater London. Visiting this gem of a binocular shop provides an evocative throwback to times past for binocular enthusiasts (◆ see box).

While antique shops and fairs used to be good places to find binoculars, in recent years it has become difficult to find material of interest, even at the larger events. It is possible to walk round the thousands of stalls at such events as the Newark International Antique Fair and still only see a small number of binoculars – mostly poor quality Galilean types.

In London, most collectors head to the famous Portobello Road street market in the north-west of the capital, where a bustling atmosphere is guaranteed from the early hours, every Saturday morning. Here, it is possible to see the wares of sellers such as 'big' Bill Kilby (◆ see box). Large-scale military festivals such as the UK's 'War and Peace' event, held each year in Kent, do provide collectors of military optics with a regular staging point in their year.

MY BINOCULAR STORY

The sad binocular

A PAIR OF binoculars everyone – engineers, housewives, farmers, schoolteachers – should have a look through is the 8x50 Nobilem Special, made by Carl Zeiss Jena in the early 1980s. It's a great binocular, if only for size: you need large hands to get to the focus wheel properly.

All things great become even greater when they're tragic. Take the Nobilems, they symbolize the tragedy of Carl Zeiss Jena – once the most respected optics plant on earth – like no other binoculars. With the Nobilems Zeiss Jena tried to prove they were still capable of manufacturing the world's finest optical instruments. And so, in the early 1980s, they did what they were

really good at – manufacturing binoculars of awesome construction and optical quality. They threw some big size prisms in, and large eyepieces, because that's what you need for a really superb view.

However, it was all to no avail. The world no longer seemed interested too much in qualities like that. As Leitz 20 years earlier in the early 1960s had proven ever so clearly, the public's demand had changed from serious instruments for hunting to more frivolous, leisure time toys. People of the 1980s liked their binoculars to be light, compact and handy.

Didn't Zeiss Jena notice? The answer is, I think, that even if they did, they were unable to do

something about it.

Imagine an East German company really thinking about and working hard on marketing. I think it was beyond their power, maybe even beyond their imagination. Marketing, I think, is the challenge of getting to the people, asking questions, listening carefully, then starting to think about optimization (and so, about compromises). But the question is, can you see this challenge? I don't think at Jena they could. So that's where Zeiss Jena suffered, went into decline, and eventually lost: in marketing.

When I see a CZJ Nobilem I can't help but be reminded of the Cold War, the partitioning of Germany, the Corridor and the Wall.

I think CZJ Nobilems are the saddest binoculars in history.

Renze de Vries

A VISIT TO KAY OPTICAL

THE SHOP IS reached by taking the London Underground's 'Northern Line' as far south as it goes. When I visited the shop on a dreary October day, it took some time to realise I had indeed found its first floor headquarters. It felt like I'd stumbled into one of the residential flats that line London Road in this part of the commuter belt. As I negotiated my way past six-foot high piles of binoculars and telescopes, mixed up with numerous boxes and miscellaneous paperwork, owner Tony Kay greeted me.

This is far from a conventional binocular shop. Although dealing in new optics for over thirty years, the shop has long specialised in used binoculars and telescopes too. So successfully, that Kay Optical now has the UK's largest retail collection of second-hand binoculars. Starting out in business in 1962, the company originally repaired and serviced binoculars of pre-war vintage. Much of the equipment during the early years was of British, French and German origin, but with the Japanese binocular boom of the late 1960s, servicing work expanded considerably. Gradually, further types of optical servicing were added (such as telescopes and microscopes), in particular the servicing of ophthalmic instruments for lens manufacturers and opticians.

Due to popular demand, the sales of binocular and telescopes began in the 1970s – especially for birdwatchers. In the 1990s, the company diversified further through the addition of a dedicated astronomical section. Forty-five years after the company was founded, binoculars remain a key focus of the company.

On the day of my visit the three first floor rooms were crowded with plastic crates, all crammed full of optics recently brought back from one of the company's 'field days'. Held at nature reserves in Southern England, these events – pioneered by Kay Optical – allow customers to choose binoculars in authentic outdoor settings. As Tony began to reveal the story of his businesses my eyes darted about, fixing on scarce and collectable binoculars wedged into every available space. I noted the tell-tale squat case of a Zeiss West 8x30 from the 1960s – and couldn't stop myself from teasing apart the lid to reveal a beautifully preserved binocular within, nestling like a polished pearl inside its shell. Everywhere I looked there were other optical gems to be discovered. I lifted some papers to find a well looked-after Leitz 8x20 pocket binocular – its optics still capable of rendering exquisite images of the capital's skyline

outside the window. I dug deeper beneath a pile of paperwork and came across sumptuous leather cases from more high quality glasses – some of which I did not recognise. I felt like the proverbial child inside a sweet shop.

I was keen to have a look at several noteworthy used models which were detailed on the company's website. Tony took my list and kept retreating into the darkened corners and anterooms of his shop, only to emerge with an exciting binocular in his grip. Some had special stories of their own to tell – such as a rare war time 7x50 model made by Nippon Kogagu, a company that was later to form part of Nikon.

Formerly something of a collector himself, Tony has gradually sold off his binocular collection to fund business expansion. Not surprisingly, the impressive array of new and used optics now attracts a loyal group of regular customers, including some avid collectors.

BB

➧ *www.kayoptical.co.uk*

At a time when binocular collecting was becoming a difficult hobby to pursue due to a lack of suitable retail outlets for used models, eBay came along to rekindle the interest of many enthusiasts. It is difficult to underestimate the importance of eBay in once again exciting interest in binoculars as collectables and allowing so many second-hand binoculars to be brought together for sale at the click of a mouse.

An unusual collectable binocular from the 1960s incorporating a radio in its case. The binocular is a Japanese-made 7x35 instrument of impressive optical quality, made by Sunscope

The author was delighted when a US eBay seller enclosed this additional gift when sending him a binocular from across the Atlantic

MY BINOCULAR STORY

Taking a closer look

MARTIN ROBERTS, proprietor of Woodnook Antiques in Otley, has an unconventional use for binoculars during his visits to major antique fairs across the country – he uses them to scan distant stalls for possible bargains, before homing in on the most interesting-looking items! The huge Swinderby International Antique Fair takes place on the runways of a disused airfield, and the first things that Martin buys when he arrives on site are a binocular and a bicycle. The event is so large that visiting the many thousands of stalls on foot is exhausting. Instead, Martin cycles round the airfield, scanning along each row of stalls to check for unusual items. A recent find was a scarce onion vase which he picked out on a stall through his binocular from some distance away, and then sold on to a collector, making a healthy profit. Martin certainly has an eye for a bargain: in 2008 he paid £50 for a tray of silver at a clearance sale, only to discover a rare Egyptian alabaster figure dating back to 1386 BC among the lot. A few months later the tiny figure was sold for over £30,000 at the top London auction house Christie's.

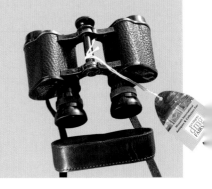

BILL KILBY – KING OF BIG BINOCULARS

BILL KILBY MUST be one of the few people in the UK to make his living entirely from selling second-hand binoculars. His company, Horizon Antiques, has established itself as a leading provider of large ex-military binoculars and his eye-catching stock takes pride of place in one of the main thoroughfares of London's Portobello Road antique market.

Although Bill lives in Devon he spends most Saturdays in the capital at the famous Portobello market. Formerly a butcher, Bill has built up his successful business over ten years, first trading in small binoculars, telescopes, microscopes and scientific instruments but now concentrating mainly on large binoculars. Bill currently employs ten people, among them surely the last used binocular-buying apprentices in the country. Bill specialises in high quality, high

price stand-mounted binoculars, such as the 10x80 aerial observation models that were once used in operations against the British air force over the skies of Germany.

Many of his binoculars have been transformed by careful polishing of their original military colours to reveal the shiny metal covering that lies beneath. They make an imposing statement in the picture windows of rich city apartment owners who visit the market in search of items on which they can lavish their pay bonuses. Other people, such as interior designers, also buy these beautiful instruments as if pieces of sculpture, using them to add decorative flourish to executive homes. Bill and his team make special metal housings and tripods for many of the large binoculars as the original wooden ones are not thought to be as well made as

the binoculars themselves and are certainly not as decorative.

Bill's large binoculars do come with the advantage of free postage and packing to any destination in the world, which often results in instruments finding their way to exotic destinations, a fortnight or so after their new owners parted company with £3,000 during their holidays in London. Bill also sells to dealers overseas. He remembers vividly one Saturday morning when he sold £75,000 worth of binoculars to a New York buyer in the space of a few minutes. All were subsequently sold on in the USA within a month!

Horizon Antique's company's motto, 'Looking through to the past', sums up the dual appeal of historic binoculars: antiques with stories to tell that can also be wonderful observation tools.

Begun in 1995 the on-line auction site eBay has quickly grown to spectacular proportions, with an income higher than the Gross Domestic Product of some nations. On the day the author wrote this chapter there were, on UK eBay alone, 1544 binoculars up for auction, including 58 by Zeiss (mostly second-hand) and many models from makers which are now all but impossible to find in shops or fleamarkets.

The success of eBay has allowed enterprising binocular enthusiasts to make a living or supplement their income by buying and selling binoculars through the site. eBay buyers are attracted to trusted sellers and some of those with the highest counts for positive feedback can command a premium on their binoculars. This is helped by their friendly attitude to sellers, detailed close-up photographs of the items for sale and comprehensive and authoritative texts to accompany the listings.

A collectable 1960s Tasco binocular camera, featuring a miniature 110 camera combined with a compact 7x20 binocular. This particular model was used by James Bond in a big screen movie featuring 007

MY BINOCULAR STORY

Eric Wood – trusted eBay binocular seller

ERIC WOOD IS perhaps the UK's best-known eBay binocular trader, whose carefully photographed and meticulously-described instruments attract bidders from all over the world. But his first experiences of using binoculars came before the computer was even invented and are linked to an unconventional use of binoculars while on two wheels.

The love affair begins

Though now retired and living in rural Cornwall, Eric spent much of his youth in the city of Manchester. He first got interested in binoculars in 1948, when he joined the Youth Hostel Association in order to enjoy some longer cycling excursions with a local group. Every weekend the group headed out into the hills surrounding Manchester, finding a hostel where they could spend Saturday night. A friend of Eric's during these excursions always used to keep a small binocular in his cycle bag – a Zeiss 4x20 model as he recalls – and Eric was surprised at how impressive even a binocular of only x4 magnification could be at getting close-up views of the countryside and wildlife. So began a sixty year love affair with binoculars.

Moving up the gears

As soon as he could afford a basic binocular of his own Eric invested in a simple second-hand Galilean model, as he could not afford anything special as a working class teenager in 1950s Britain. His first prismatic binocular came a few years later in the form of a compact Kershaw 8x21, which he still remembers as an impressive binocular. Around this time Eric became interested in fell-walking, spending many weekends in Derbyshire, the Yorkshire Dales and the Lake District, all within easy reach of his home in Manchester. He was able to enjoy the landscapes of these dramatic

IMAGE: BARBARA WOOD

parts of England in even more exquisite detail following his acquisition of a pre-war uncoated Carl Zeiss Jena 8x30 Deltrintem, which he bought second-hand from a Manchester camera shop.

It was only in 1970 that Eric could afford to buy his first new binocular, and he continued to be faithful to Zeiss by choosing a 8x30 Jenoptem model, which cost him £37, not an insignificant sum at this time, yet presenting an excellent image for the price. Eric still thinks that Zeiss Jena models of this period – especially the later multi-coated versions – represent some of the best value used binoculars that are currently available. By this time Eric had been very much bitten by the binocular bug, and he began 'trading up' in order to obtain better examples of key instruments, as a fledgling collection started to take shape.

From collector to seller

By the time he had retired in 1995 from a career in technical development and quality control in the textile industry, Eric had a small collection of high quality binoculars which included a 10x50 model from Zeiss Jena and an 8x30 model from Zeiss West. Another hobby of Eric's – book-collecting – led him to discover the online auction site eBay in 2000 where he began browsing through second-hand binoculars. The mouth-watering collections of optics were tempting, and Eric realised that he could continue experimenting with various models and types, selling on those that did not impress. It was an ideal way of trying all the binocular models on the market at the time. It then became apparent that buying wisely and selling carefully could actually bring a small profit on each instrument sold, helping Eric to earn some 'pocket money'.

Eric experimented with several accounts and had some terrible

experiences in the early days of eBay, when there were many rogue traders and the feedback system was simply not respected. Things improved and slowly, as his experience and mastery of the eBay listing process increased, Eric began to buy binoculars just to sell on and realised that he could add significantly to his pension through this exciting online activity.

Eric identified the use of high quality photographs and a very careful description as two keys that could unlock the potential of eBay for a seller. As his positive feedback increased, so he found regular customers returning to him, allowing Eric to develop a separate business outside eBay trading in binoculars. In tandem with his wife, Barbara, Eric now sells around five binoculars a week on eBay throughout the year. Barbara assists by selling binoculars through her own account and by taking responsibility for packing up all the binoculars and carting them to the post office once a week.

His knowledge of the hidden places of eBay and its worldwide influence mean that Eric has managed to find some amazing bargains. One example is the poorly-described and mis-spelled Swarovski 10x25 which he bought for £70 one week and sold for £260 two weeks later. However, he continues to find eBay prices unpredictable. The same item can sell for a different price every week! Eric has also developed an international network of scouts who find scarce or exotic optics in a range of overseas locations.

eBay frustrations

Eric has a key note of caution for anyone new to eBay or those wanting to get most enjoyment out of the site: always check a seller's feedback ratings very carefully before making a bid. This extends beyond the more obvious percentage ratings to

MY BINOCULAR STORY *Continued*

checking how many binoculars, or other items of similar value, the person in question has sold recently. Sellers may get consistently good ratings for their CD sales, but could know nothing about binoculars and list items that are not worthy of their descriptions! Knowing who you are buying from is one of the essential ingredients of successful eBay trading.

Despite now being much more established as a presence on the internet, Eric admits that he still finds eBay a frustrating place to do business. There is insufficient protection given to buyers, and even less to sellers, compensation for bad transactions often being inadequate and difficult to obtain. The new feedback system also places far too much power in the hands of the buyer and no redress for the seller. This is

all made much worse by the fact that the faceless customer support team – who seem to all read from the same script – are in the main incapable of resolving genuine concerns. Eric believes that eBay gives you a simple choice: continue using it with all its foibles, or find somewhere else to buy and sell binoculars. Worryingly, Eric's attempts to make careful and well-documented complaints to eBay have fallen on deaf ears, a sure sign that this enormous company is losing touch with the very people that helped make it successful in the first place.

Eric's favourite binoculars

Eric must have handled thousands of binoculars since he first peered through that Zeiss binocular on a cycling trip sixty years ago. He has also spoken or corresponded with hundreds of

binocular enthusiasts, collectors and users and he is mindful that people's personal choice of optics is a very complex and individual matter. Indeed, an important part of the service he offers is to advise customers on the factors involved in choosing binoculars and the pitfalls of buying. Yet his favourite models – and those that he keeps in his treasured personal collection – still come from Germany, surely the spiritual home of binoculars. Eric's current binocular of choice is the Leica Ultravid 8x32, which he considers offers superb image quality, coupled with an incredible fidelity of colour rendition not seen in some other high-end binoculars. He is looking forward to using the latest version of this instrument which incorporates High Definition glass to boost image quality still further.

While this is not the place to reveal too many insider secrets, binocular enthusiasts have managed to unearth a wealth of important instruments through eBay, many of which escaped the attention of less knowledgeable people. The author has not found any spectacularly unusual binoculars on this auction site, but did manage to buy a museum quality Zeiss 6x30 Silvamar from the 1920s. This was poorly photographed and mistakenly listed under the heading of a cheap 1970s binocular, whose instruction book had somehow found its way into the Zeiss leather case.

The average price for a binocular sold on eBay over the last few years is £42.33. Sellers of binoculars on this auction site report that many buyers of binoculars seem to exist in something of a bubble that is cocooned from the prevailing economic climate. The author can certainly confirm that prices for the more sought-after models continue to hold their own in the UK, despite weekly warnings that the country is in the firm grip of a major 'credit crunch' and destined for a recession. The eBay phenomenon has also started to bring a degree of standardisation to the prices paid for second-hand binoculars, aided by the ability to search for completed transactions to see what buyers have recently paid. While this might appear to offer some benefits, it means that buyers are less likely to find bargains now that anybody in the world can check what specific models have been selling for.

eBay deserves a special mention here for another reason – there is no doubt that the author would not have been able to produce the book in your hands without the help of this extraordinary website. Most of the binoculars in his reference collection were originally found on eBay and his own sales there have helped to finance the acquisition of new instruments and the publication of the book. Furthermore, many of the advertisements and photographs featured in the book were bought through the site. eBay is also the place to meet like-minded enthusiasts and collectors – the author also found some of his most valued correspondents through communication about items up for sale.

Perhaps the reason that eBay is so addictive is that it offers for collectors the world's biggest virtual flea market specialising in their specific interest. All you need to do to enter this fascinating world is to key in the appropriate keywords. But be warned: once entered the world of eBay is very hard to leave!

Binoculars for everyone

Some collectors enjoy acquiring binoculars as 'objets d'art' rather than because of their optical qualities. It is now possible to buy reproduction or 'antiqued' brass binoculars in a variety of sizes for less than £50, no doubt all made in China. Some models even come on impressive wooden tripods. While there are actually lenses in these instruments, in most cases people purchase them as décor for their living rooms rather than actually to look through them.

The highly polished ex-military binoculars sold by Bill Kilby on London's Portobello Road can be both 'objets d'art' and regularly-used instruments, depending on the owner. For some binocular enthusiasts, the destiny of many

Binoculars sold on eBay can end up in some interesting locations. Among the 500 or so examples sold by the author after his reference collection was broken up was this Zeiss Jena 10x50 Jenoptem, which found its way over the Atlantic. A message from the purchaser read – 'My father received them and was extremely pleased with the quality. He lives on a farm overlooking the Mississippi river in Iowa and can now watch bald eagles hunting around the river as well as other wildlife'

MY BINOCULAR STORY

Binocular memories

MY GRANDFATHER GAVE me an old Zeiss Deltrintem when I was about seven. I remember it well because from the first time I looked through it from our balcony at golfers on the green I was amazed that I could clearly see into the distance. He purchased it second-hand on the way home from work on a Friday and gave it to me the next morning. My parents, being European immigrants in a new house, saw them as being old binoculars and had him return them on the Monday. Because this made me sad they bought me some nice new Japanese binoculars. I still have them thirty-six years later, but I never forgot the Deltrintem and have had one for the last twenty-three years.

Michael Kaczor

AN EXTRAORDINARY FIND

AN AMAZING DISCOVERY was made in England in 2008 when an extremely rare Carl Zeiss Jena binocular of giant proportions was offered to the Devon-based nautical antiques shop Trinity Marine. The binocular, a triple power (x35, x58 and x117) Zeiss Asal model with 130 mm objective lenses, is so large it needs to be housed on a massive metal mount and tripod. The new price for this binocular in the 1935 was $2,772 and there exist photographs of it in use at mountain viewing points in the Alps. There is thought to be just one other example of this binocular in existence. For those collectors tempted to acquire this sensational instrument, a large bank balance will be needed: its selling price is £45,000. Anyone who is lucky enough to own this binocular, however, knows that they are never likely to be upstaged in the binocular stakes.

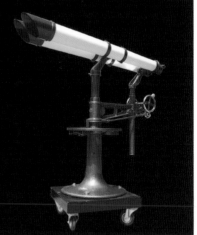

Tiny 'binoculars' which present the user with images of Capri (Italy), when held up to the light. Early versions of such devices, fashioned from bone or ivory, were sometimes called 'Stanhopes' after a British maker

large war-time binoculars is now a sad one. Stripped of their original paint, markings and accessories, many are destined to spend their lives as ornaments on the desks or in the apartments of American executives, who pay top dollar for these buffed-up binoculars. They are sometimes even ruined optically as the heat produced by the buffing dissolves the balsam in the lenses and creates unwanted internal condensation.

The research necessary for this book led the author to a range of other binocular-themed items, many of which tested the limits of taste. Chief among these is an Avon-branded aftershave and eau de cologne set contained in a curious binocular-shaped flask. Surely even the most hardened binocular collector would not want this kitsch item to be awaiting him under the Christmas tree.

Binocular miniatures and replicas intended for use in conjunction with children's action figures are commonly found. Included in this category are

LEFT: Binoculars without lenses sometimes find their way into the homes of people who collect other objects. This strange object is a ceramic model of a binocular, which came from a collection of items designed to imitate various instruments, called the 'vintage collection'

RIGHT: A binocular-shaped clock, ideal for the mantelpiece of binocular enthusiasts

delightful Russian 'Action Man' binoculars, complete with their tiny leather case. Vintage versions of such accessories sometimes fetch more on the collectibles market than the binoculars themselves! Numerous soft toys – many aimed at collectors rather than children – have been issued in special editions sporting binoculars. This means that in the secret cupboards of teddy bear collectors you may find animals proudly sporting binoculars of various shapes and sizes, frequently with matching outdoor clothing. Designers have also used binoculars to inspire a range of flasks and other drinks containers. Some are even used to disguise the fact that alcohol is being smuggled into venues where this is not permitted.

Just how many binocular collectors will be putting this Avon aftershave and eau de cologne set on their Christmas lists this year?

'I have a 1/12th scale set of binoculars made specially for the lighthouse keeper in my dolls' house lighthouse, by a firm that makes miniature glassware for dolls' houses.'
GILL O'DONNELL

Binoculars have had a starring role in many novels and feature films, as well as acting as 'extras' that movie prop coordinators bring out before the cameras for their cameo roles. In M.R.James's chilling short story *A View from a Hill*, the bones of ex-criminals are boiled to form a liquid which is then stored inside the binocular of a principal character, causing him to see horrific sights relating to their activities. Looking through the eyes of dead men eventually destroys this evil man, the sprits of the deceased killing him. There are also several children's books which, thankfully, feature binoculars in less scary ways.

The use of binoculars in film and other visual media has led to the manufacture of a further range of binoculars without lenses – from pin badges featuring Micky Mouse to Star Wars spaceships that transform into binoculars. It seems

Miniature binoculars for use by children using action figures

BINOCULARS WITHOUT LENSES

THE FACT THAT binoculars have established themselves as important consumer items means that it is possible to find an impressive array of objects inspired by binoculars that do not in fact possess any lenses. Some of these are cute, others quaint and a final group plain bizarre. Perhaps most frequently found in antiques shops are 'cruet sets' (salt and pepper containers) which mirror the shape of Galilean binoculars. These must have been produced in huge

numbers as holiday gifts, and were often finished off with the names of popular seaside resorts. Other, stranger ceramics include intriguing copies of war-time binoculars designed for display, which have been deliberately distressed to look old.

Ceramic binocular-shaped salt and pepper sets are commonly found, with this kitsch example marked 'Greetings from Brighton'

The author pictured with binocular-shaped drinking vessels in a Finnish barbeque hut known as a 'grill kota'

that marketing departments are prepared to churn out anything that stands a chance of selling, and a binocular theme can provide a distinctive angle to any new product.

Some wonderful examples exist of cards and postcards from around the world that depict binoculars in use – frequently in amusing situations. Some of the most charming are surely those showing Father Christmas as he keeps his eyes on the delivery of presents. The author has reused these, for friends and family, almost a century after they were first created, as amusing throwbacks to times of old. The tradition of binoculars on cards continues into the 20th century. The author met a lady who was inspired to make a birthday card using a toy Barbie's binoculars, and his own 40th birthday card was an inspired creation from his wife! (see page 187).

Some advertisers have used binoculars to add a certain style or mystique to other products. While a few of these products have obvious associations with binoculars, others seem just to use them as 'window dressing'. The resulting printed advertisements sometimes become collectibles in their own right.

There are many pin badges inspired by binoculars, which find their way into the collections of people who do not otherwise have an interest in optics

"Tropic Ice"... in cool Wash and Wear sport shirts

Just like turning on the "cool" switch. Thousands of tiny ventilators refresh you the moment you put on one of these air-spun cotton coolers.
And this "Sanforized" 100%-cotton "Time-Saver" fabric can be washed just as you please. Wash by hand, or wash and dry by machine, using the new wash-and-wear cycle. Not even the touch of an iron is needed. If you must go out into the hot sun, this is your shirt.
Available in white, frosty pastel shades and smart fashion-trim effects on pockets and sleeves. Price, a cool $4.00.   *Cluett, Peabody & Co., Inc.*

ARROW first in fashion

Three ways in which advertisers have used binoculars to help market their products. The colour card from France states that 'Sunlight soap is the best'

The politically incorrect 1970s allowed companies to use advertising methods that would be frowned upon today. The cigarette manufacturer Camel has, nevertheless, managed to weave an amusing visual gag here in this 1971 offering, which also shows the stereotypical two barrelled view of what you see through a binocular

Various 21st century companies use binocular associations on advertising material, despite the product having nothing to do with optics

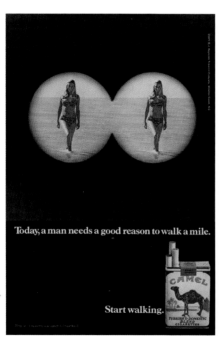

Today, a man needs a good reason to walk a mile.

Start walking.

LOOK **NO** FURTHER...

...VIEWING ONLY

With over 70 realistic **KITCHEN** and **BEDROOM** roomsets under one roof you simply must visit CROWN in DAVENTRY. To book your viewing call Sophie on 01227 742424.

www.crown-imperial.co.uk

CROWN IMPERIAL

IMAGE: CROWN PRODUCTS (KENT) LTD

A montage of images from postcards and greetings cards showing the diverse ways in which binoculars are used to help convey messages

I WONDER THERE HASN'T BEEN COMPLAINTS ABOUT THESE MEN UNDRESSING WITH THEIR BLINDS UP.

"IF YOU GET OUT YOUR LONG DISTANCE BINOCULARS, YOU'LL SEE US HAVING THE TIME OF OUR LIVES!"

"YOU'D LOOK TWICE AS NICE IF I COULD SEE YOU CLOSER"

Mein tut mir beständig weh, Weil ich kein lein von Dir feh!

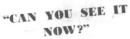

"CAN YOU SEE IT NOW?"

GOOD LUCK!

I'm looking forward to seeing you at SOUTHEND-ON-SEA

I send you Good Luck,
And my wishes sincere,
Raise the round flap,
And twelve views will appear

Epilogue

Will special eye implants one day allow people to see the world through their own in-built binoculars? What other technological improvements might revolutionise binocular design in the future? Might computer technology one day even make binoculars redundant? These are just some of the questions to be explored in this epilogue which considers the fascinating topic of the evolution of binoculars in years to come. While we cannot, of course, provide a blueprint for the future of binocular design, we can certainly speculate on the innovations that may lie ahead. These will, themselves, eventually form part of the history of people and binoculars.

Binocular design has benefited from a host of innovations since the first crude instruments were conceived and finally constructed over four centuries ago. Each has sought to bring special benefits to users, and by the early 21st century has brought binocular performance close to the theoretical maximum. Indeed, some binocular experts believe that we may have already reached a plateau in terms of the performance of binoculars that do not benefit from in-built computer technology. British optics expert Steve Harris has termed this the 'binocular glass ceiling'. It seems that the latest generation of instruments from the top makers may have improved in some critical respects, but represent a step backwards in others. This is despite their price creeping above and beyond the formidable £1,500 mark as the book went to press. We may already be on the cusp of seeing all future non-computerised binocular design representing a compromise between one optical property or another.

The quest for optical perfection

Light gathering power is a key factor governing the performance of binoculars, since brighter images render more detail and a more impressive viewing experience. Since the invention of optical coatings in the late 1930s, manufacturers have been nudging light transmission figures close to and – with the latest Fujinon models enhanced by their patented electron beam coatings – beyond the 95% level. It is impossible to predict how much closer to the holy grail of 100% is possible as new coating systems are developed, but what is sure is that even with 5% more light transmission the next generation of binoculars are not going to be spectacularly brighter than those currently available. As such, it is clear that the step change from the era prior to the development of coatings (with about 50% light transmission in the best optics) to the current performance levels can never be repeated. Instead, manufacturers will have to look to other innovations in order to create the next phase of binocular design history.

One of the principal quests of binocular designers in recent years has been the reduction in so called 'chromatic aberration' – the colour fringing that appears around the edge of subjects viewed through a binocular. This phenomenon is caused by the way in which optical glass focusses light; it has the effect of reducing image quality and during long-distance work even renders some binoculars as virtually unusable. Highly expensive fluorite crystal or fluoride elements have been used in the last decade or so in select high-end binoculars to minimise this problem. In other binoculars special glass (known as ED or Extra Low Dispersion glass) that reduces the unwanted colour fringing has been introduced. These developments have added to the cost of some binoculars, but discerning observers have appreciated the optical improvements they have heralded. Future developments are sure to see work aimed at eliminating such chromatic aberration still further.

The future is stabilised

If the purpose of a binocular is to enable the user to see more, then the evolution of binoculars surely lies in models that incorporate image stabilisation devices. The author's personal experience of birdwatching with a stabilised Canon 10x30 shows that such a binocular consistently allows you to identify more species and pick out more detail of subjects than with a conventional binocular, unless it is placed on a tripod.

At the time of writing Canon is the only manufacturer that has produced lightweight image stabilised binoculars of low to medium power. Those made by Fujinon and Nikon are bulky, heavy and unlikely to be carried on long walks or birdwatching trips. The Canon range – which includes five models from x8 to x18 magnification – sells extremely well and it seems only a matter of time before one of the top European brands produces a rival product. The fact that Canon has chosen to produce its stabilised binocular in one of Japan's top optical plants ensures that it has at its heart a unit with superb optical qualities as well as fine lens coatings, which can only be further enhanced by the stabilisation feature.

Computer technology

We are living during a technological revolution, with computers and microchips transforming every aspect of our lives. To date, however, this technology has yet to get itself *inside* many binoculars. While a few models incorporate digital cameras, generally to poor effect, manufacturers have yet to explore the possibilities of such advances as computer-enhanced images or even software that can recognise particular birds or mammals being observed. There are clearly complex design hurdles to be overcome before these advances can be made, and they seem unlikely to be conquered in the next few years. Yet they provide pointers towards a future that some pioneering designers may be able to bring closer.

We can go further by suggesting that computer technology may, in fact, have the potential to eventually make binoculars obsolete in some situations. It is perhaps in the military arena, where government expenditure on research exceeds that which can be carried out by individual manufacturers for the civilian market, that such a breakthrough is most likely. High quality computer-aided devices for observing the battlefield from a ground-based or aerial position may yet consign field observers with binoculars to the annals of military history. The rise in optical quality of everyday consumer devices such digital cameras shows how computer technology can transform what we can see and capture electronically. Furthermore, we are already witnessing the incredible surface detail which can be seen with the new generation of earth observation satellites. The ability to track individual people in real time on the ground from space – James Bond fashion – may be only a few years away.

Medical procedures

The brain is an amazing organ. It has the ability to turn what we see through the lenses in our eyes from an inverted to an upright view of the world. In fact, during experiments where subjects wear spectacles that render an inverted view, the brain has been shown to have the incredible ability to reverse this to produce a normal picture after a few days. Binoculars can, then, just be considered rather crude devices that allow our amazing brains and eyes to do their work better.

If a binocular is a merely an optical device for seeing more, then if special implants are placed in people's eyes might it be possible for them to see a magnified view of the world – to possess their own built-in binocular? This might appear like Million Dollar Man science fiction, but it seems that it is not beyond the bounds of medical science to replace or augment the human lens with a natural (perhaps from another animal) or man-made structure that results in increased magnification. The experiments referred to earlier suggest that the brain might be able to accommodate such procedures.

The author has actually sometimes wondered whether every human already sees the world at the same magnification. This thought was first triggered by his father-in-law, who has such acute vision that he seems to see the world a little closer than anyone else! The possibility remains that at some time in the future a person, possibly for military or sporting purposes, might be equipped with their own 'implanted binoculars'. Bizarrely, there could even be options for interchangeable magnifications!

The rise of China

There is no doubt that the country of China will dominate binocular production for the foreseeable future. The combination of state-of-the-art production methods and comparatively low factory wages mean that Chinese-made instruments of exceptional value are certain to continue appearing on the market. While some of those currently on the market seem to be very good clones of models produced by well established manufacturers in other countries, there are genuine breakthroughs and innovative designs now emerging from China. As this book went to press a Chinese roof prism binocular of very high quality was launched – at a price that could see other high-end manufacturers scratching their heads over how they can compete. The fact that the Chinese-made Nikon Fieldscope 50ED has quickly become the instrument of choice for weight-conscious bird-watchers wanting a small telescope, shows that if quality can be guaranteed buyers are more than happy to buy from China.

While there will always be some purchasers who stay loyal to the European brands, even hardened users of products from such famous companies as Zeiss may be prepared to jump ship if the price is right. Indeed, the price of the high-end models from the top four manufacturers continues to rise inexorably, beyond what seemed possible only a few years ago. Whatever the fortunes of specific new models from China, it is clear that four hundred years after the invention of the binocular in Europe, the power balance is shifting from this continent to the Far East. The large numbers of Chinese spectators seen using binoculars at the Beijing Olympic Games surely hint at a new era to come.

A vision for the future

Throughout this book, the author has tried to show the diverse ways in which people have interacted with binoculars at work and at play over four centuries. It is clear that these ingenious optical devices have enhanced the lives of millions of people across the world. But it is also clear that binoculars can be much more than everyday possessions that people treasure – they can also be vital tools that can save lives and help people make the world a better place for us all.

As the rest of the 21st century unfolds, they are likely to become even more widely owned as the price of basic models continues to tumble. Microsoft, the global computer software giant, had a vision in 1980 of 'a computer in every home'. Like computers, binoculars allow people to enter into another domain – to see the world in new ways. It will be fascinating to see how much closer we are by the middle of the century to the vision of 'a binocular in every home'. Surely, many wonderful new stories await us of people and their binoculars.

The author's 40th birthday card, conceived and hand crafted by his imaginative wife Amanda

Glossary

Achromatic lens – a *lens* is described as achromatic if two widely spaced wavelengths of light are focused into the same image plane. Achromatic lens elements consist of at least two slices of glass that have been cemented together or are separated by a layer of air. Such lenses are used in binoculars to improve optical quality and were first developed in Britain by Chester Hall Moore in about 1729.

Alignment – see *collimation*.

Apparent field of view – the visible breadth, usually expressed in degrees, as seen through a binocular. It can be approximated by multiplying the real field of view in degrees by the *magnification*.

Apparent magnification – the phenomenon of higher power binoculars not rendering more detailed images due to *binocular shake*. For example, although x10 binoculars have an ability to see more detail, binocular shake can reduce their performance to the same apparent magnification as a x8 or x7 binocular.

Aspherical lens – a *lens* with a surface profile that is neither a portion of a sphere nor of a cylinder. Such lenses are used to reduce optical aberrations.

Barium crown glass – a type of high quality glass used to make binocular *prisms*. Prisms made with such glass are termed BAK-4.

Binocular – an optical and mechanical instrument which uses two rigid parallel tubes, in combination with *lenses* and/or *prisms*, in order to make objects appear closer to the user when viewed with both eyes. Note that the grammatically correct form for the singular of the instrument is 'a binocular' not a 'pair of binoculars', though the latter is in common usage and has become standard form among laypeople. [➤ see also *monocular*]

'Binocs' – a shortened form of the word *binocular*.

'Binos' – a shortened form of the word *binocular*.

Binocular (or hand) shake – the slight trembling of the hands when using binoculars, usually of higher *magnification*, that results in the image appearing jumpy and sometimes out of focus.

Binoculars – the plural of *binocular*, i.e. one binocular, but two binoculars.

'Bins' – a shortened form of the word *binocular* which is especially popular with birdwatchers in the UK. For example a birdwatcher might say, 'There's a raptor soaring overhead, can you get your bins on it?'.

Brightness – literally how bright the image appears when looking through a binocular, which is linked to the ability of a binocular to deliver light to an observer's eyes (➧ see also *light transmission*).

Central focussing (CF) – a type of focussing arrangement which uses a wheel to control both optical tubes of a binocular to bring objects of varying distance into sharp focus.

Collimation – a binocular is said to be 'in collimation' when both optical barrels point at exactly the same spot, providing the observer with a perfectly spherical view when using the instrument. Binoculars that are 'out of collimation' give double images and can induce eye-strain as the brain tries to form a single image. The term 'alignment' is used synonymously with collimation.

Colour fringing – see *chromatic aberration*.

Contrast – the ability of a binocular to differentiate between the dark and light elements of a subject. Binoculars render better images when they have increased contrast.

Chromatic aberration (colour fringing) – the appearance of coloured edges to subjects viewed through a binocular, caused by the way in which light is bent by *lenses*. Some makers use *high definition* or *extra low dispersion glass*, or *fluorite* crystal, to control this effect and improve optical quality.

Dioptre adjuster – a mechanism, incorporated in most *central focussing* binoculars, that allows for the different visual acuity in an observer's eyes to be accommodated, thereby bringing subjects into sharp focus in both optical tubes. Dioptre adjustments are often made by rotating one of the eyepieces.

Extra low dispersion (ED) glass – special glass used in some high-end binoculars in order to reduce *chromatic aberration*.

Eyepiece focussing – see *individual focussing*.

Eyepiece lens – see *ocular lens*.

Eye relief – the distance between the surface of a binocular's *ocular lens* and the point at which the whole *field of view* can be seen clearly. Eye relief is particularly important to spectacle wearers, as they cannot get their eyes as close to the lens surface as other users.

Exit pupil – the circular disk visible on the surface of the eyepieces when a binocular is held about 30 centimetres away from an observer towards a bright light. Its diameter, in millimetres, is worked out by dividing the aperture of the *objective* lens by the *magnification*. In general the larger the exit pupil, the brighter the image to be seen through a binocular.

Field glasses – an archaic name for a *binocular*, most frequently referring to those of *Galilean* construction.

Field of view – the angle of the field visible through a binocular, as measured from the central point of the *objective lenses*. The larger the value, the wider the field of view and the easier it is to locate objects. Field of view is sometimes expressed in the number of meters or feet at 1,000 units distance.

Fixed focus binocular – a binocular which has no means of focus adjustment and it set to be sharp from about 10 metres to infinity.

Flourite – a type of mineral used in very expensive optical devices to improve image quality. Chemically a calcium fluoride, fluorite occurs naturally as crystals, but is also grown in laboratories for use in optics. It suffers less *chromatic aberration* than standard optical glass and is therefore an ideal, if costly, alternative. Because good quality fluorite crystals are hard to find and can be difficult to handle, some manufacturers treat glass with fluorine ions, which give it similar properties to fluorite, but make it chemically more stable and easier to shape.

Galilean binocular – the simplest type of binocular incorporating a concave *lens* closest to the eye and a convex lens at the opposite end of the instrument. Named after the early pioneer of astronomy with a telescope, Galileo Galilei (1564-1642).

Graticule – a scale engraved on a plate of optical glass which is located at the focal plane and which allows the distance of objects to be estimated. Known as a recticule or recticle in the USA.

High definition (HD) glass – special glass used in some, mostly high-end, binoculars in order to reduce *chromatic aberration*.

Individual focussing (IF) – a type of focussing arrangement which uses the two eyepieces to bring objects of varying distance into sharp focus. Sometimes called *eyepiece focussing*.

Image (or field) flattener – a special *lens* element which results in increased edge-to-edge sharpness in certain models of binocular.

Keplerian binocular – a simple type of binocular which uses a convex *lens* closest to the eye and another at the opposite end of the instrument. Such binoculars produce an inverted view, which can be corrected by the incorporation of *prisms*. Named after the German mathematician and astronomer Johannes Kepler (1571-1630) [➤ see also *Galilean binocular*]

Lens – a component in a binocular made of high grade optical glass.

Light transmission – the amount of light, usually expressed as a percentage, a binocular is capable of transmitting from the outer surface of the objective lenses to an observer's eyes.

Magnesium fluoride – a white crystalline salt and the original ingredient in optical coatings applied to *lens* and *prism* surfaces to improve *light transmission* in binoculars. More recent *multicoatings* contain several layers which are of varied chemical composition.

Magnification – a number given to a binocular to signify the amount of times closer to the observer objects appear when viewed through the instrument. For example, viewing through a x10 binocular objects that are 1,000 metres away appear as if they were only 100 metres away.

Monocular – one half of a *binocular*.

Multicoating – the application of several layers of *magnesium fluoride* and other chemicals on the *lens* or *prism* surfaces of binoculars to improve light transmission. State-of-the-art binoculars can have upwards of 20 such layers on one glass surface.

'Nocars' – (pronounced knockers) a shortened form of the word *binoculars* which is much less commonly-used than the terms *bins* or *binos*. Its use, especially by women, brings with it humorous overtones due to the implied anatomical innuendo.

Objective lens – the *lens* furthest away from the user. Light from subjects hits the objective lens first before entering the body of the binocular and many binocular objective lenses have large diameters to increase light input.

Ocular (eyepiece) lens – the *lens* closest to the eyes of the user.

Opera glass – a small, low power *Galilean binocular* designed for use in the theatre.

Optical coating – a special chemical layer (originally of *magnesium fluoride*) which is applied *lens* and *prism* surfaces in order to improve the *light transmission* of a binocular.

Optical munitions – optical instruments designed especially for military uses. They include binoculars, gun-sightings telescopes, rangefinders and submarine periscopes, all of which incorporate precise optical systems and are designed to withstand adverse conditions not encountered by optical devices made for commercial use.

Phase contrast coating – a coating applied to *roof prisms* to improve image quality.

Porro prism – type of *prism* developed by the Italian optical pioneer Ignazio Porro (1801-1875). It gave rise to the familiar bent body-shape of binoculars launched by Zeiss in the 1890s and which is still a common form today.

Prism – a glass structure that bends light and is capable of inverting an image in optical instruments. Their invention gave rise to the first prismatic binoculars, which appeared in the late 1800s.

Prismatic or prism binocular – a type of binocular that uses *prisms*.

Prism plate – a flat piece of metal which conceals the *prism* cluster of a binocular. Binoculars usually have both front (closest to the *objective lens*) and rear (closest to the *ocular lens*) prism plates. This structure is sometimes simply called a 'cover plate'.

Resolution – the ability of a binocular to pick out fine detail. Though resolution differences between different models are usually apparent to most users in normal use, they can be tested more objectively using a variety of special charts.

Roof prism – a type of *prism* that results in a more streamlined body shape in binoculars than that possible in *Porro prism* models. Roof prism binoculars were pioneered in the late 1890s by the German maker Hensoldt and are now one of the most popular types of binocular.

Waterproof – a binocular is said to be waterproof if it is sealed against the ingress of water. Most waterproof models can be immersed fully in water without it entering the body of the binocular.

Wide-angle binocular – a binocular is generally considered to have a wide angle if it has an *apparent field of view* of at least 60 degrees, though the Japanese Industrial Standard sets the mark at above 65 degrees.

Zoom binocular – a binocular which uses additional 'floating *lens*' elements in order to enable the user to vary the *magnification* of the image. Owing to the difficulty of constructing such a binocular and the need for large *objective lenses* at high magnifications, zoom binoculars are not usually very effective.

Places to visit

There are only a handful of places where it is possible to see a range of binoculars on display, and even fewer where visitors are able to actually look through instruments of interest. As binocular historian William Reid has so eloquently said, 'Strangers to the subject must find it incredible that more binoculars can be found at an average antiques and collectors' fair than are to be seen in some major institutions devoted to the history of science.' I list below the principal museums of interest for those who seek out binoculars.

Optical Museum, Jena

Showcasing over 1,500 optical instruments over eight centuries and including many interesting binoculars from the works of Carl Zeiss Jena. The museum gives a technical and cultural-historical survey of the development of optical instruments.

Optisches Museum, Carl-Zeiss-Platz 12, 07743 Jena, Germany

www.optischesmuseum.de/museum.html

Military Museum, Koblenz

Though mainly specialising in large military hardware such as tanks and other vehicles, the museum also holds a collection of military optical devices, including binoculars. This is the only place in the world where you can see the enormous war-time Zeiss 20/40x200 binocular telescope on display.

Wehrtechnische Studiensammlung, Mayener Straße 85-87, D-56070 Koblenz, Germany

Optical Museum, Oberkochen

Featuring the progression of the telescope and binoculars since the 17th century, this museum, owned by to the Carl Zeiss optical giant which has its base in the town, also boasts an impressive collection of artefacts. It includes many modern binoculars that are not housed in the optical museum in Jena.

Optisches Museum, Carl-Zeiss-Straße 22, 73447 Oberkochen, Germany

Imperial War Museum, London

A small selection of binoculars, including some owned by famous military figures, are found in the rather dimly-lit display cases. An interesting exhibit features optical devices used in war.

Imperial War Museum, Lambeth Road, Southwark, London, SE1 6HZ, UK

www.iwm.org.uk

National Army Museum, London

A few binoculars are on display, including most notably those owned by celebrated nurse and writer Florence Nightingale.

National Army Museum, Royal Hospital Road, London, SW3 4HT, UK

www.national-army-museum.ac.uk

National Media Museum, Bradford

Many of the binoculars previously housed in the Science Museum are now held in this museum in the north of England.

National Media Museum, Bradford, West Yorkshire, BD1 1NQ, UK

www.nationalmediamuseum.org.uk

Rosebud County Museum, Montana

Includes a collection of antique binoculars and opera glasses, loaned by Steve Kaluza.

Rosebud County Museum, Forsyth, Montana, USA

Teylers Museum, Haarlem

Displays scientific instruments from 1800-1900, including binoculars and telescopes.

Teylers Museum, Spaarne 16, 2011 CH Haarlem, Netherlands

www.teylersmuseum.nl

IMAGE: STEVE KALUZA

Websites

Better View Desired

www.betterviewdesired.com

This American site contains a wealth of interesting material on binoculars. The most helpful articles are the reviews written by the site's founder, Steve Ingraham, who now works for Zeiss. Many people believe that his articles on binoculars on this site are some of the finest ever written.

Birdforum

www.birdforum.net

Billed as 'the net's largest birding community' there is much to engage the binocular enthusiast on this very extensive site. Some of most interesting content can been accessed by studying the forum postings on optics, and you can join the online community to contribute your own ideas.

Cloudy Nights

www.cloudynights.com

A site for astronomy enthusiasts, with extensive information on optics. This is a great place to visit to learn about some of the latest products on the market, with reviews appearing almost as soon as new binoculars appear.

Fan Tao

http://fantao.home.att.net

A very informative website containing photographs and accounts of some of the more interesting items in Fan Tao's binocular collection. Many landmark binoculars are included and the site is a great place to browse through some of the finest models ever made.

Holger Merlitz

www.holgermerlitz.de

German university physics professor Holger Merlitz has written some of the most thorough comparative reviews of binoculars on the web. His site also contains useful background articles on a range of other binocular-related topics.

Bibliography and further reading

Abrahams, P. (1996) The early history of binoculars. *Amateur Telescope Making Journal* 9.

Alexander, J. (2002) Nikon and the sponsorship of Japan's optical industry by the Imperial Japanese Navy, 1917-1945. B.C. *Asian Review* 13 (Spring 2002): 1-21.

Akin, A. (1994) *Optics for Birding.* Wolfe Publishing.

Anonymous (1969) Binoculars. *Which? Magazine* June 1969.

Anonymous (1974) *Popular Optics.* Edmund Scientific.

Armstrong, A. (1990) *Binoculars for Birders: a field guide to binoculars.* Avian Press.

Auerbach, F. (1925) *The Zeiss Works and the Carl Zeiss Foundation.* Foyle.

Barsness, J. (1999) *Optics for the Hunter.* Safari Press.

Brown, E. (1949) *Basic Optics for the Sportsman.* Stoeger Arms.

Chandler, D., Chandler, B. & Davis, D. (2005) *Exploring the Night Sky with Binoculars.* David Chandler Company.

Cherrington, E.H. (1985) *Exploring the Moon Through Binoculars and Small Telescopes.* Dover Publications.

Conder, P.J. (1963) Buying Binoculars. *Junior Birdwatcher.* Vol. 5, No. 1:10-12.

Cooper, J. (1965) *Photography Through Monoculars, Binoculars and Telescopes.* Chilton.

Corbett, B. (2003) *A Simple Guide to Telescope, Spotting Scopes and Binoculars.* Amphoto books.

Crossen, G. & Rhemann, G. (2003) *Sky Vistas: Astronomy for binoculars and richest-field telescopes.* Springer-Verlag.

Crossen, G. & Tirion, W. (1992) *Binocular Astronomy.* Willman-Bell.

Flegg, J. (1972) *Binoculars, Telescopes & Cameras for the Birdwatcher.* British Trust for Ornithology.

Geer, G.L. & Geer B.E. (1990) *The Wildlife Observer's Eyes: optical equipment for observing nature.* Menasha Ridge Press.

Gould, J.A. (1977) The large German binoculars of World War II. *Journal of the British Astronomical Association* 85:393-400.

Gregory, R.C. (2003) *Notes on Binoculars and Their Use.* Amwell Books.

Gregory, R.C. (2003) *The Finest Optics for Birdwatching: a critical appraisal.* Amwell Books.

Gregory, R.C. (2004) *Fine Binoculars of the Twentieth Century.* Amwell Books.

Gregory, R.C. (2005) *Binoculars: a pocket guide.* Amwell Books.

Gubas, L.J. (2004) *An Introduction to the Binoculars of Carl Zeiss Jena 1893-1945.* Privately published.

Hale, A. (1991) *How to Choose Binoculars.* C&A Publishing.

Harrington, P.S. (1990) *Touring the Universe through Binoculars: a complete astronomer's guidebook.* John Wiley and Sons.

Hawkins, G. (2007) *Novelties: the story of the Leica Trinovid.* Privately published.

Hebditch, J.R. (1965) *Binoculars and Telescopes for Fieldwork.* British Trust for Ornithology.

Henson, T. (1955) *Binoculars, Telescopes and Telescopic Sights.* Greenburg Publisher.

Huff, E. & de Vries, R. (2005) The inimitable Swift Model 804 Audubon binoculars: design and marking variations. *Article published by the authors on www.birdforum.net.*

Kozak, J.T. (1998) *Dee-Sky Objects for Binoculars.* Sky Publishing Corporation.

Lutes, J. (2000) *Lookout Training Handbook.* Naval Education and Training Professional Development and Technology Center.

Mensing, S. (1988) *Stargazing Through Binoculars: complete guide to binocular astronomy.* TAB books.

Moore, P. (2000) *Exploring the Night Sky with Binoculars.* Cambridge University Press.

Mosley, J. (1998) *Stargazing with Binoculars and Telescopes.* Contemporary Books.

Moss, M. and Russell, I. (1988) *Range and Vision: the first hundred years of Barr & Stroud.* Mainstream.

Mullaney, J. (2007) *A Buyer's and User's Guide to Astronomical Telescopes and Binoculars.* Springer-Verlag.

Muirden, J. (1988) *Astronomy with Binoculars.* Prentice Hall.

Paul, H.E. (1980) *Binoculars and All Purpose Telescopes.* Amphoto.

Peltier, L. C. (1995) *The Binocular Stargazer: A beginner's guide to exploring the sky.* Kalmbach Publishing.

Rees, C. (2004) *Optics Digest.* Safari Press.

Reichert, R.J. & Reichert, E. (1963) *Binoculars and Scopes and Their Uses in Photography.* Amphoto.

Reid, W. (1982-5) Binoculars in the army. *Army Museum Bulletin* 1982: 10-23; 1983: 15-30; 1984: 39-53; 1985: 31-39.

Reid, W. (2001) *We're Certainly Not Afraid of Zeiss: Barr & Stroud binoculars and the Royal Navy.* Museum of Scotland.

Reynolds, M. (2005) *Binocular Stargazing.* Stackpole Books.

Robinson, L. J. (1990) *Outdoor Optics: choosing and using binoculars, spotting scopes and more.* The Lyons Press.

Rohan, S. (2002) *A Guide to Handheld Military Binoculars 1894-1945.* Optical Press.

Rohan, S. (1996) *Eyes of the Wehrmacht: an illustrated guide to the German World War II 10x80 binoculars.* Optical Press.

Scagell, R. & Frydman, D. (2007) *Stargazing with Binoculars.* Phillip's.

Seeger, H.T. (1987) *Feldstecher: ferngläser im wandel der zeit.* [Fieldglasses: binoculars through history]. Bresser.

Seeger, H.T. (1993) 100 years of prismatic binoculars. *Bulletin of the Scientific Instrument Society* 37: 16-18.

Seeger, H.T. (2005) *Militärische Ferngläser und Fernrohre in Heer, Luftwaffe und Marine* [Military Binoculars and Telescopes for Land, Air and Sea Service]. Privately published.

Sell, F. (1970) *Hunting with Camera and Binoculars.* Amphoto.

Seronik, G. (2007) *Binocular Highlights: 99 celestial sights for binocular users.* Sky Publishing Corporation.

Serviss, G.P. (1888) *Astronomy with an Opera Glass.* Appleton.

Seyfried, J.W. (1995) *Choosing, using and repairing binoculars.* Altantic Books.

Tonkin, F.T. (2006) *Binocular astronomy.* Springer-Verlag.

Watson, F. (1995) *Binoculars, Opera glasses and Field glasses.* Shire.

Watson, F. (2000) The dawn of binocular astronomy. In: *2001 Yearbook of Astronomy.* Trans-Atlantic Publications.

Index